The Open University

Science: a level 3 course

Understanding the Continents

Block 3

Growth and Destruction: Continental evolution at subduction zones

Prepared for the Course Team by Stephen Blake and Tom Argles

G000231190

The S339 Course team

Chair
Nigel Harris

Course Manager
Jessica Bartlett

Other members of the Course Team

Mandy Anton *(Designer)*

Tom Argles *(Author)*

Gerry Bearman *(Editor)*

Stephen Blake *(Block 3 Chair, Author)*

Steve Drury *(Author)*

Professor Wes Gibbons, University of Wales, Cardiff *(Course Assessor)*

Nigel Harris *(Block 4 Chair, Author)*

Lee Johnson *(Graphic Artist)*

Martin Kemp *(BBC Producer)*

Dave McGarvie *(Author)*

Jann Matela *(Word Processing)*

Ray Munns *(Cartographer)*

Pam Owen *(Graphic Artist)*

Ian Parkinson *(Reader/Author)*

Professor Julian Pearce, University of Wales, Cardiff *(Course Assessor)*

Nick Rogers *(Block 2 Chair, Author)*

Hazel Rymer *(Block 1 Chair, Author)*

Val Russell *(original Course Manager)*

Andy Sutton *(Software Designer)*

John Whalley, University of Portsmouth *(Consultant Author)*

The Course Team gratefully acknowledges the contributions of those who produced the first editions of this Course, from which parts of this Block have been derived. In addition, we would like to thank the students, Associate Lecturers and assessors from other institutions who commented on drafts of this new edition. Other contributors to S339 are acknowledged in specific credits.

The Open University, Walton Hall, Milton Keynes MK7 6AA.

First published 2003.

Copyright © 2003 The Open University.

All rights reserved. No part of this publication may be reproduced, stored in a retrieval system, transmitted or utilized in any form or by any means, electronic, mechanical, photocopying, recording or otherwise, without either the prior written permission of the publishers or a licence permitting restricted copying issued by the Copyright Licensing Agency Ltd. Details of such licences (for reprographic reproduction) may be obtained from the Copyright Licensing Agency Ltd. of 90 Tottenham Court Road, London W1P 0LP.

Edited, designed and typeset by The Open University.

Printed in the United Kingdom by Bath Press, Blantyre Industrial Estate, Glasgow G72 0ND

ISBN 0 7492 5666 4

This block forms part of an Open University course, S339 *Understanding the Continents*. The complete list of texts which make up this course can be found at the back. Details of this and other Open University courses can be obtained from the Course Reservations and Sales Office, PO Box 724, The Open University, Milton Keynes MK7 6ZS, United Kingdom: tel. (00 44) 1908 653231. For availability of this or other course components, contact Open University Worldwide Ltd, Walton Hall, Milton Keynes MK7 6AA, United Kingdom: tel. (00 44) 1908 858585, fax (00 44) 1908 858787, e-mail ouwenq@open.ac.uk

Alternatively, much useful course information can be obtained from the Open University's website, http://www.open.ac.uk

3.1

Contents

1 Introduction and study comment

The purpose of this Block is to investigate the processes that generate and modify the Earth's continental crust at subduction zones. Whereas divergent plate boundaries involve the generation of oceanic lithosphere and the splitting of continental lithosphere, it is at convergent boundaries where much of the tectonic, metamorphic and igneous turmoil that leaves its imprint on the geology of the continents is active. In Block 4, you will study the processes associated with continent–continent convergence; but in this Block, you will concentrate on the Earth's subduction zones.

Subduction zones are recycling sites for Earth materials. Subduction of oceanic lithosphere carries mid-ocean ridge basalt (MORB) and residual mantle that formed below mid-ocean ridges by partial melting of the mantle back into the mantle. This, however, is not a simple conveyor-belt transport of mid-ocean ridge igneous rocks from ridge to trench to mantle. Chemical alteration by rock–seawater interaction in the hot and corrosive environment of mid-ocean ridge hydrothermal systems, and the accumulation of deep-sea sediment, mean that the subducted materials are a modified version of the materials extracted from the mantle at the ridge. As well as receiving materials at subduction zones, the mantle also loses material in the form of the magmas that produce volcanic arcs — one of the most distinctive geological features associated with subduction zones. These magmas intrude the crust and erupt onto its surface, while tectonic movements thicken, thin, and re-organize the crust. Within and near the trench, vast volumes of sediment are tectonically assembled in accretionary prisms. It comes as no surprise that subduction zones are involved in both the destruction and growth of Earth's lithosphere.

Figure 1.1 shows the anatomy of a generalized subduction zone in cross-section and relates this to the topics of the sections in this Block. Section 2 presents an overview of the components of subduction zones, revising some points you will have already met and bringing together information from different subduction zones to establish a simple but interesting observation — no two subduction zones are the same. Just as 'variety is the spice of life', the variety among subduction zones makes for interesting comparisons and revealing insights into how continents form and evolve. The rest of the Block progresses from looking at the individual components of subduction zones in isolation to learning how

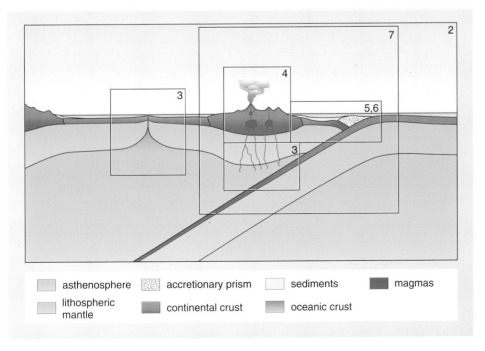

asthenosphere   accretionary prism   sediments   magmas

lithospheric mantle   continental crust   oceanic crust

Figure 1.1 Generalized cross-section of a subduction zone. Numbered boxes refer to Section numbers in this Block.

they are linked together. Section 3 dwells on processes that generate magmas in the mantle at subduction zones. Section 4 follows the magmas upwards, and describes the chemical composition and mineralogy of volcanic rocks found in subduction zones. Here you will learn about the processes occurring within arc volcanoes and how they can be recognized from geological evidence. Section 5 deals with the fate of sediment that enters subduction zones. Here you will investigate the origin and deformation of accretionary prisms — the great accumulations of sediment scraped from the sea-floor when subducting oceanic lithosphere grinds against a plate margin as it starts to sink into the mantle. Whether or not any sediment escapes this trap and enters the mantle, contributing to magmas erupted at the surface, is an interesting puzzle which is also addressed in Section 5.

Sections 6 and 7 move on from looking at currently active subduction zones to ones where plate convergence has ceased and the results of prolonged subduction are visible. In Section 6, geological evidence for growth of continents by the tectonic addition of crustal slices and blocks is explored. Section 7 links the previous Sections together by discussing how magmatism and tectonics at subduction zones conspire to build new continental crust. Part of this story of continental growth involves huge volumes of plutonic rocks — the subsurface complement to the volcanoes seen in active subduction zones.

In studying this book, you will encounter the geology of Santorini volcano (in the Aegean Sea), California, and the Andes. Activities in the Block will involve you in replicating part of a subduction zone with some common household items, studying thin sections of metamorphic and igneous rocks using the *Digital microscope* on CD-ROM, handling data, reading scientific literature, and a video field trip to Santorini.

2 Observations

This Section introduces the main components of destructive plate margins, and assesses the variation in the phenomena and processes associated with them. The aim is both to build on concepts such as back-arc extension and accretionary prisms introduced in Block 1, and to provide a foundation for more detailed study of specific aspects later in this Block.

Section 2.1 gives an overview of the fundamental geometry and dynamics of destructive margins, moving on in Section 2.2 to examine the lithosphere overriding the subducting plate. Sections 2.3 to 2.5 then describe three different aspects of the subduction zone system: the accumulation of material near the trench (accretionary prisms), subduction-related magmatism (volcanic arcs) and extension behind the arc (back-arc basins).

2.1 Modes of convergence

Simple plate geometry and dynamics exert a profound influence on both the form of an arc system, and the processes by which it evolves. For example, not all subducting plates approach their respective destructive margins perfectly head-on, and of course the convergence rate varies too, both in time and space. This Section looks at some of these basic features of arc systems.

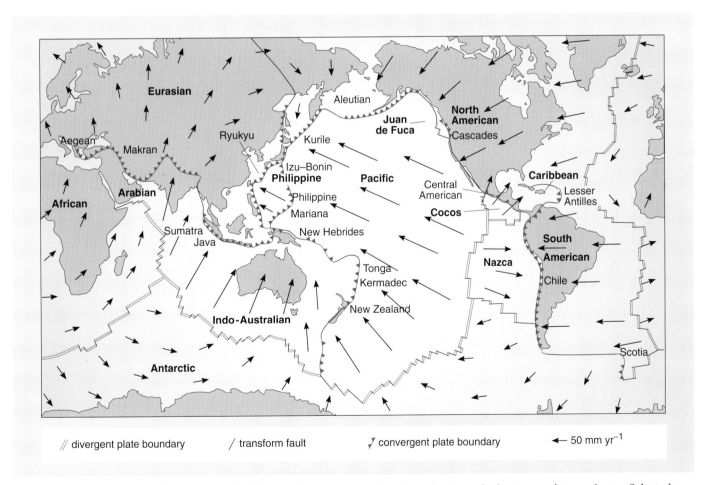

| // divergent plate boundary | / transform fault | ⌇ convergent plate boundary | ← 50 mm yr⁻¹ |

Figure 2.1 Map of the world showing plate boundaries and plate velocities, relative to the hot-spot reference frame. Selected convergent boundaries where oceanic lithosphere is being subducted are named in plain type; bold type identifies plate names. Arrow lengths are proportional to plate speeds.

2.1.1 Geometry of destructive plate margins

Trench shape and subduction angle

You may have noticed, either on Figure 2.1 or during your study of Block 1, Activity 1.2, that most destructive margins (comprising parallel arc–trench systems) trace out curved lines on maps. Why are these plate boundaries arcuate? Well, their form stems from the geometrical rules that rigid plates must follow on a spherical body like the Earth. In this case, arcs are the inevitable geometry of subducting the rigid oceanic plate from the sphere's surface into its interior. There is a very simple way of demonstrating this. Take a football (or any hollow, squashable ball) — a ping-pong ball is excellent provided it is expendable! If you press a thumb into the surface, you make a curved impression in the sphere. The deeper your thumb presses in, the wider the impression. Figure 2.2a illustrates the effect; it is as if there were an invisible sphere intersecting the ball, and the circular line of intersection on the ball's surface represents the trench formed if the whole depressed area was 'subducting' under your thumb. This depressed surface is analogous to the oceanic lithosphere that has been subducted into the Earth. The curvature of the 'trench' formed in the three ping-pong balls shown in Figure 2.2a is different in each case. In fact, the curvature decreases from the left-hand to the right-hand examples. The angle of subduction (δ) increases from left to right across Figure 2.2a, so this illustrates a simple geometrical rule — arc curvature increases as subduction angle decreases.

Figure 2.2 (a) The ping-pong ball model is based on the geometry of a rigid spherical shell depressed into a sphere. Plan views and cross-sections for three dents of increasing size. Note that the radius of the intersecting sphere remains the same, but the dip angle of 'subduction' (denoted by the Greek letter delta δ) increases with the size of the dent. (b) A larger subducted area can be accommodated by splitting the intersection line into a series of arcs and cusps, preserving relatively gentle subduction angles.

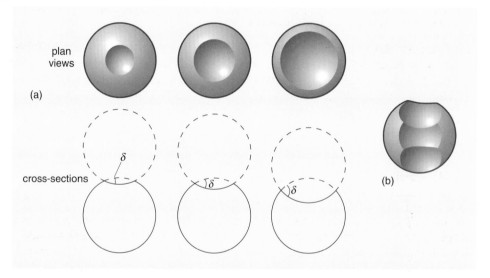

To accommodate a larger depressed area (i.e. a particularly large plate), several adjacent trench–arc systems separated by cusps can form, as if several 'dents' had been made in the ball (Figure 2.2b).

- Can you identify a region on Figure 2.1 where several arcs are linked by similar cusps to those in Figure 2.2b?

- Many of the arcs in the western Pacific are linked at cusps like this. Particularly striking is the margin from the Aleutian Islands in the north, along the Kurile Islands and Izu–Bonin arcs to the Mariana arc north of Papua New Guinea. These linked trenches trace out a series of cusps rather like the right-hand edge of the dents in Figure 2.2b.

● Why do you think this geometry has developed in the western Pacific?

● All the arcs mentioned above are located along the margin where the vast Pacific Plate is subducted below other plates further to the west. The margin has split into shorter segments to accommodate the subduction of the Pacific Plate more easily.

Can the dip of the subducting plate be predicted in a similarly simplistic way from the behaviour of a ping-pong ball? As described in Block 1, pinpointing the subsurface locations of earthquakes in **Wadati–Benioff zones** allows quite precise mapping of the form of subducting slabs — they represent some of the most seismically active zones on the Earth. The information in Table 2.1 is based on such data.

Table 2.1 Geometrical characteristics of some arc–trench systems.

Arc–trench system	Subduction angle	Curvature
Mariana	80–90°	highly arcuate
Lesser Antilles	45°	moderately arcuate
Tonga	45°	low curvature
Kurile*	35–50°	moderately arcuate
Northern Chile	10–30°	low curvature

* The Kurile Islands have the distinction of being the arc where Hugo Benioff first mapped the subduction zone at depth using earthquake data.

Question 2.1 Study the information on subduction zone geometry in Table 2.1 and Figure 2.2 in the context of the geometrical rules of the ping-pong ball model. For each of the following subduction zones, explain how they obey or contravene the rule relating trench (and thus arc) curvature to subduction angle.
(a) Mariana.
(b) Lesser Antilles.
(c) Tonga.
(d) Kurile.
(e) Northern Chile.

The ping-pong ball model is moderately successful at explaining the geometry of subduction zones, but why is it not always successful? Often, models break down because one or more simplifying assumptions in the model are not met. One assumption of the model is that the plates are inextensible (rigid), and that they must subduct as slabs with an equal and opposite curvature to their original form. However, seismic evidence suggests that they do deform, which explains why some arcs disobey the simple ping-pong ball rules. Where the dip is too steep, subducting plates tear, and a gap appears in the earthquake distribution (Figure 2.3a). Compressed plates, for instance where subduction is too shallow, may buckle and fold (Figure 2.3b). This may also happen if there is not enough space for the downgoing plate, as appears to be the case with the Philippine Plate beneath central Japan (Figure 2.3c), and the southern end of the Lesser Antilles arc.

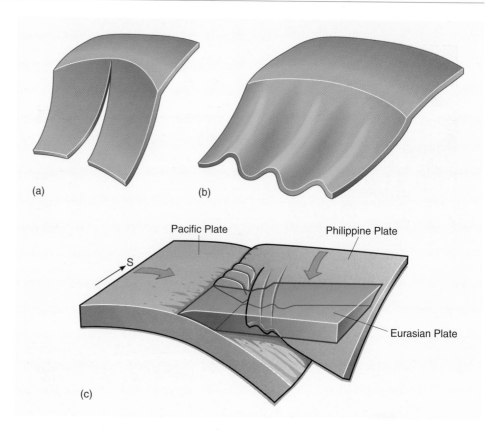

Figure 2.3 Subducting slabs under tension and compression develop (a) longitudinal tears or (b) buckle folds respectively. This often relates to dip angle: too steep brings tension, while too shallow results in compression. (c) Block diagram showing a southward-looking view of the possible situation where the Philippine Plate subducts below the Eurasian Plate (shown in brown) in the vicinity of Japan. The subducted Philippine Plate is forced to contort as a result of interference from the subducted Pacific Plate.

Angle of plate convergence

● Is convergence always orthogonal (at 90°) to the arc?

● No, it seldom is — witness the Kurile arc on Figure 2.1. Oblique convergence is quite common.

Even if trenches were straight lines, there is no reason for a subducting plate to approach the margin head on. Because the direction of plate motion varies only gradually across a plate, it follows that only a limited section of an arcuate trench will experience orthogonal convergence — either side of this, convergence will get more and more oblique as the arc curves round. In Figure 2.4a, convergence around the Lesser Antilles arc becomes so oblique at the extreme N and S ends that the subduction zone passes into strike–slip faults that define the northern and southern boundaries of the Caribbean Plate.

A survey of currently active volcanic arcs implies that the downgoing plate must approach at a relatively high convergence angle (>25°) to the plate boundary for magmatism to occur; in systems with more oblique convergence, arcs are weakly developed or absent. In terms of structures, oblique convergence results in a zone with a mixture of compressional and strike–slip deformation, known as **transpression**. The two styles of deformation generally occur separately; they are said to be **partitioned** (separated into two components). Thus, compressional structures might be concentrated in the **accretionary complex**, while a strike–slip fault accommodates the transcurrent component of the motion. The natural place for this fault is at the rear of the accretionary prism, isolating a fore-arc sliver in front of the main arc (Figure 2.4b). Extensive slip on this fault, due either to long duration of motion or high obliquity of convergence, may lead to huge lateral displacement of the fore-arc sliver, and its emplacement as an exotic **terrane** along strike. This mode of accretion is explored in Section 6.1.

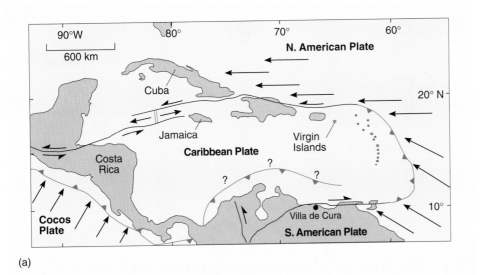

(a)

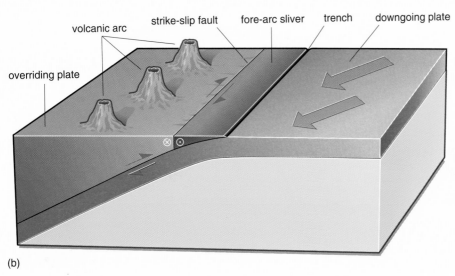

(b)

Figure 2.4 (a) Simplified map of the Caribbean region, showing the changing angle between the direction of plate motion and the trench, culminating in an essentially pure strike–slip boundary from the Virgin Islands to Cuba. Villa de Cura is a locality famed for metamorphic rocks formed during subduction, and these are mentioned in Section 6. (b) Model for processes at oblique subduction zones, showing partitioning of the plate motion direction into dip–slip and strike–slip components. Note that the relative movement across the strike–slip fault is indicated on the cross-section by circular symbols denoting motion into the page (circle with cross) and motion out of the page (circle with dot). The strike–slip fault isolating the fore-arc sliver commonly forms at the rear of the accretionary prism, as in the Ryukyu arc system.

Angle of slab descent

Another variation in subduction zone geometry is the angle of slab descent. The answers to Question 2.1 imply that this angle is not always related to arc curvature in the simple way predicted by the ping-pong ball model. In fact, subduction dip has been shown to vary considerably, not only from slab to slab, but also both with depth and along strike within single slabs. Further evidence strongly suggests that subduction dip also varies over time as a convergent margin evolves.

> **Question 2.2** (a) Briefly state how information on the shape of subducting slabs can be obtained. (b) What additional data can be used to determine whether specific portions of the subducting slab are in compression or tension?

Compilations of data from first-motion studies show that some parts of subducting plates are in tension, while others — even in the same slab — are under compression. Figure 2.5 illustrates some of the variety in the dip of the subducting slab and its state of stress. There is a general tendency for extension in the upper slab and compression at greater depths, but this depends partly on how the angle of descent changes with depth; some dips increase (Mariana), a

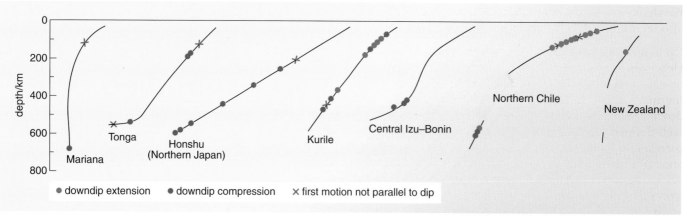

Figure 2.5 (a) Cross-sections through some of the world's Wadati–Benioff zones, based on observed seismicity. The first motions of earthquakes along the zones indicate whether the downgoing slabs are in compression or extension. Note that this information is restricted in both space and time: quantitative earthquake data are confined to depths shallower than about 600 km, and for the last 100 years or so.

1ˢᵗ signal arrival –

upward = compressional.
downward = dilational.

Block 1 p.16

few decrease (Tonga), yet others show a sigmoidal shape (Izu–Bonin). There are seismic gaps in some slabs (Northern Chile), suggesting breaks or discontinuities of some kind; these are sometimes known as 'slab windows'. The cause of these changes in dip are obscure — they may reflect abrupt regional tectonic shifts (e.g. collision), or relative displacement between the top and base of the slab. Some evidence for this comes from seismic images of the slab under north-eastern Japan, which show two distinct bands of earthquakes with opposite first motions — perhaps representing the top and base of the subducting plate. These stresses may be related to the bending of the plate, for instance due to the gravitational force exerted by the weight of the slab itself (slab–pull force, F_{SP}: Block 1, Section 1.3). If this force is particularly strong, the dip angle will be steep, and the 'hinge' of the downgoing slab (where it starts to bend into the subduction zone) may even retreat from the overriding plate, a process known as **slab rollback**. With all these interrelated factors, it is not surprising that the ping-pong ball model is too simplistic to explain all the variations in arc geometry.

Consider for a second what determines the magnitude of the slab–pull force. It is primarily the weight of the material already subducted — provided it is still attached to the subducting plate. This depends on the volume and density of the subducted material. In Block 1, you learnt that the oceanic lithosphere becomes both thicker and colder as it moves away from the spreading centres where it is generated (i.e. as it becomes older).

- Would you expect the average density of oceanic lithosphere to increase or decrease as it gets older?

- Old oceanic lithosphere is colder than newly formed lithosphere, and so will be denser.

- Which would exert a greater slab–pull force: old or new oceanic lithosphere?

- Old oceanic lithosphere, because it is not only cold and therefore dense, but it is relatively thick as well. You would expect steep slab dips where old lithosphere was being subducted.

Comparing subduction dip in the Mariana arc with that in Northern Chile on Figure 2.5 seems to bear out the theory that slab–pull force influences the angle of subduction. Steep subduction occurs beneath the Mariana arc because the Pacific lithosphere is far from the spreading centre (see Figure 2.1), and thus is old, thick and dense. By contrast, relatively young lithosphere of the Nazca Plate is being subducted beneath Northern Chile, so subduction is at a shallow angle.

We shall see later in this Block that metamorphic changes in the subducting slab also increase its density, and hence the slab–pull force.

Up to now, we have mostly considered subduction down to 100 km or so. However, as you saw in Block 1, Section 1.5, **seismic tomography** models based on earthquake data are beginning to provide information on the internal thermal and mechanical structure of the mantle to much greater depths, even down to the core–mantle boundary (*c.* 2900 km). The most recent results show well-defined dipping zones of anomalously high seismic velocities that correspond to known Wadati–Benioff zones. These relatively cold, dense anomalies tally with known subducting slabs, and many extend down to the 670 km seismic discontinuity, which forms the boundary between the upper and lower mantle (Block 1, Section 1.5). Below this the picture becomes more equivocal. Some anomalies suggest that slabs (e.g. Southern Kurile, Izu–Bonin) may baulk at this level, being deflected horizontally at around 670 km (Figure 2.6). Other anomalies (Central America, Sunda) can be traced further, possibly even to the core–mantle boundary, but are more irregular and diffuse than in the upper mantle. These anomalies are unlikely to represent slabs as such, but may be a mixture of slab material and cooled mantle whose penetration through the 670 km level was driven by subduction. Clearly, such a downwelling of material must be matched by a complementary upwelling, just as in a lava lamp. In fact, there is increasing evidence both from tomography and basalt geochemistry for a similarly deep source for some mantle plumes, with a component of subducted crust involved. This implies a degree of recycling of crustal material back into the mantle, but it is unclear where this might occur. Our knowledge of the lower mantle in particular is still rather blurred, so that in recent years crucial mantle discontinuities have been proposed at a variety of levels (670, 900 to 1000, and 1600 km are popular examples!). All of these have been described as 'slab graveyards', but unequivocal evidence remains elusive.

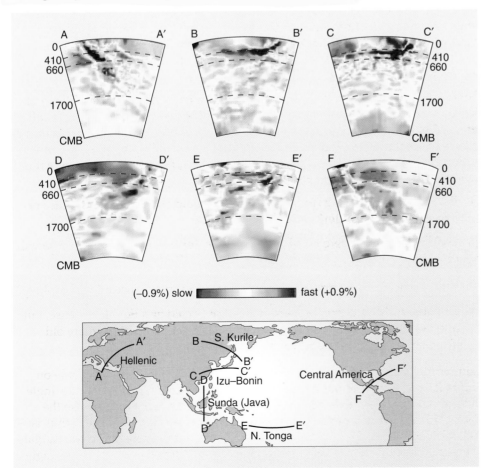

Figure 2.6 Vertical seismic tomographic slices through the mantle at the locations shown in the map underneath. Fast velocities indicate cold/dense anomalies, generally interpreted as subducting slabs or their remnants. Slow velocities imply warm, less dense material, as in mantle plumes. CMB: core–mantle boundary.

2.1.2 Rate and duration of subduction

You will have noticed on Figure 2.1 that plate velocities vary, mainly between different plates, but also (slightly) across single plates. This results in a range of subduction rates at convergent margins, from as low as 20 mm yr^{-1} at the Lesser Antilles trench in the Caribbean to over 100 mm yr^{-1} at the Chile trench. How are the magnitude and direction of these velocities determined? As discussed in Block 1, spreading rates at mid-ocean ridges can be measured fairly easily using magnetic anomalies or transform faults (and latterly the Global Positioning System, GPS). Determining subduction rates is more difficult, but since all the lithospheric plates form a mosaic on the Earth's sphere, their relative motions must all balance out (otherwise the plates would not all 'fit together'). Convergence rates are therefore usually calculated from sea-floor spreading rates using models that account for the relative motions of curved plates on a sphere. Only recently have geophysicists been able to check these modelled rates against GPS measurements.

One of the best illustrations of the importance of subduction as a driving force in plate tectonics is shown in Figure 2.7, which plots the magnitude of plate velocities against plate area, and percentage of plate circumference connected to a subducting slab. Velocity is independent of plate area, but all the fast-moving plates have proportionally more subduction around their margins. This reflects the influence of the slab–pull force (Block 1, Section 1.3).

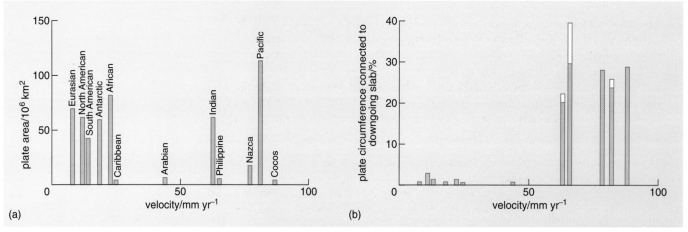

Figure 2.7   (a) Plot of plate area against plate velocity: no discernible correlation. (b) Plot of plate circumference connected to downgoing slab against plate velocity; these are strongly correlated. Open bar: total connected length; filled bar: effective length.

● Presumably, in any one plate, the subduction rate at one margin should equal the half spreading rate at the mid-ocean ridge. But is this true?

● No. If this were true, all the plates would remain the same size, neither shrinking nor expanding. In fact, subduction rates at the Pacific rim (65–106 mm yr^{-1}) are higher than the half-spreading rates along the East Pacific Rise (33–93 mm yr^{-1}).

This means that the Pacific Plate overall is shrinking, and would close completely in around 300 Ma — though this is unlikely to happen without some change in plate configuration or motion. The Nazca and Cocos Plates in the eastern Pacific are also shrinking, whereas the Antarctic and Indian Plates are growing slowly. There is abundant evidence for the complete disappearance (by subduction) of a plate known as the Farallon Plate under North America, a process which had a profound influence on the nature of the Basin and Range

Province, as you saw in the Video Band *Extensional tectonics* from Block 1. Since the oldest oceanic crust on the Pacific Plate has an age of approximately 200 Ma, the Pacific Ocean must have opened by about 200 million years ago. Adding this figure to the estimated time until its closure provides a best guess at the lifetime of a major ocean basin: approximately 500 Ma.

The discussion above considered relative plate motions, but what about absolute motions? Defining a suitable reference frame is the problem here, but one study estimating plate motions relative to the Earth's centre found that not only the plates, but also their margins, have absolute motions. For subduction zones, these are small compared to their relative motions (15–20 mm yr^{-1}), but may be significant when considering the relationship of the lithospheric plates to the mantle.

Clearly, subduction cannot continue indefinitely at the rates mentioned above; the duration of such zones must be limited. The end of a subduction zone's life usually comes via a collision with a body of thick low-density crust, and a change in tectonic configuration occurs as a result. One case where collision does not occur is when a spreading ridge is consumed by a subduction zone. This is accommodated by a change in the regional tectonic configuration, as happened when a spreading ridge was consumed in California, producing the San Andreas Fault.

● Why is subduction generally stopped by the arrival of relatively low-density lithosphere at the trench?

● The buoyancy of the material counteracts the driving forces of subduction (essentially, the slab–pull force), even though there may still be a large weight of subducted slab pulling the plate into the subduction zone. In practice, this buoyant crust will be a mature oceanic arc, oceanic plateau, or continental margin — considerably thicker than normal oceanic crust and therefore liable to jam in the trench due to its bulk. This greater thickness of buoyant crust means that the lithosphere as a whole is more buoyant in that region.

Collisions come in many shapes and sizes, some of which can be seen in Figure 2.8. In most of these cases, some kind of subduction continues after collision, but in a modified form. In part (a), subduction ceases entirely because the blocks of the (buoyant) continental lithosphere have been brought together. The resulting situation is a continental collision zone, with the location of the former ocean marked only by a **suture** between the two masses. In many cases, fragments of oceanic crust are caught up in this suture zone, giving crucial evidence for the former existence of an ocean. A famous example is the string of **ophiolites** in the Indus–Tsangpo suture zone of the Himalaya, which you will meet in Block 4. After collision, the direction of any continuing subduction (known as the **subduction polarity**) is determined by any asymmetry in crustal density across the plate boundary. The denser plate will always subduct under the more buoyant material (such as an arc or a continent).

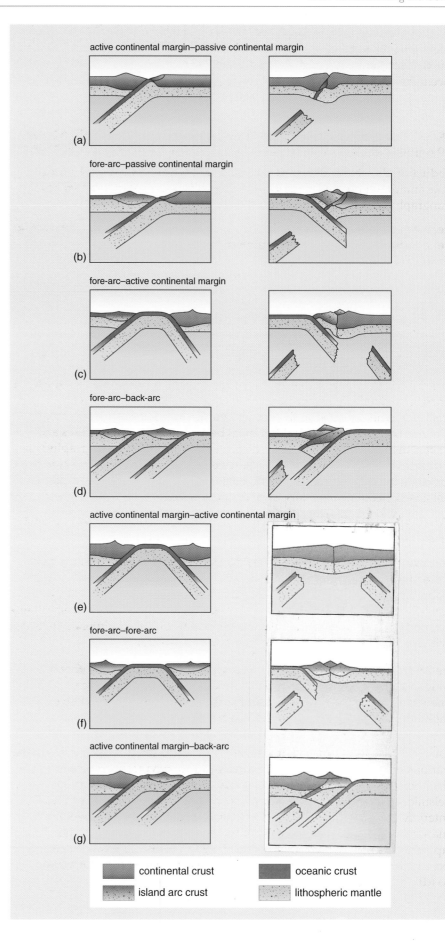

Figure 2.8 Cartoon of possible collisional situations which bring about the end of a subduction zone, in systems with (a) and (b) one subduction zone, and (c) to (g) two subduction zones. In each case, the pre-collisional stage is shown on the left, and the aftermath on the right. The diagrams are labelled according to the two types of lithosphere that are destined to collide — either continental lithosphere overriding a subducting plate (active continental), continental lithosphere attached to oceanic lithosphere (passive continental), the trenchward edge of an island arc (fore-arc), or the rear of an island arc (back-arc). Note that in several cases the lower part of the slab(s) from the abandoned subduction zones becomes detached and sinks slowly into the mantle; there is evidence for this process from seismic tomography images.

estion 2.3   Sketches of the three situations are given in
ure A2.1. Note that in the fore-arc–fore-arc collision (f),
ier oceanic plate could subduct beneath the collided arc
lowing collision. In the continent–continent collision (e), on before and after collision,
oduction ceases entirely, whereas in (g), the oceanic plate n before collision. Sketch the
 the far right will accommodate all the subduction once ich of these three cases.
 back-arc ocean has been completely consumed.

2.1.3   Summary of Section 2.1

- The arcuate form of many arcs is a consequence of subducting a rigid plate
  into a sphere, with arc curvature decreasing as the subduction dip increases.

- Subduction dip changes from slab to slab, and within a single slab both along
  strike and down the dip of the Wadati–Benioff zone, as shown by seismic
  tomography data.

- Ocean basins grow and shrink due to variations in spreading and subduction
  rate. A number of tectonic configurations can result in the end of a phase of
  subduction.

2.2   Nature of the overriding lithosphere

2.2.1   Composition and stratification of the overriding plate

The previous Section highlighted some of the considerable variation in the form
of trench–arc systems. However, one of the most obvious geographical
differences is whether subduction occurs beneath an oceanic or continental
margin. Are there fundamental differences between **oceanic island arcs** and
active continental margins, or is the distinction purely one of topography? To
what degree does subduction modify the overriding plate? The answers to these
questions lie in the realm of geophysics: a geological investigation would
require a very deep drillhole and even deeper pockets!

- What type of geophysical information would provide useful information on
  crustal structure?

- Information derived from analysis of seismic waves in the crust. Seismic
  refraction surveys image crustal structure in two ways: by identifying the
  boundaries between rock layers of contrasting seismic wave speeds, and
  establishing the seismic wave speeds of the individual layers. The speed of
  seismic waves through a rock is a function of its elastic moduli and density,
  which reflect its mineralogy and chemical composition.

Figure 2.9 summarizes the seismically determined layering in a number of
volcanic arcs, in comparison with the seismic structure of both typical
continental and oceanic interiors. Examine the similarities and differences
highlighted by the Figure, and tackle Question 2.4.

Question 2.4   (a) Briefly compare the absolute and relative thicknesses of the
various seismic layers present in island arcs and in typical oceanic crust.
(b) Briefly compare the absolute and relative thicknesses of the various
seismic layers present in active continental margins and in the continental
interior. (c) Briefly compare the crustal structures of active continental
margins and island arcs. (d) How do the seismic P-wave speeds in the
uppermost mantle in volcanic arcs compare with those beneath normal
oceanic and continental crust? (e) Suggest an explanation for your answer
to (d).

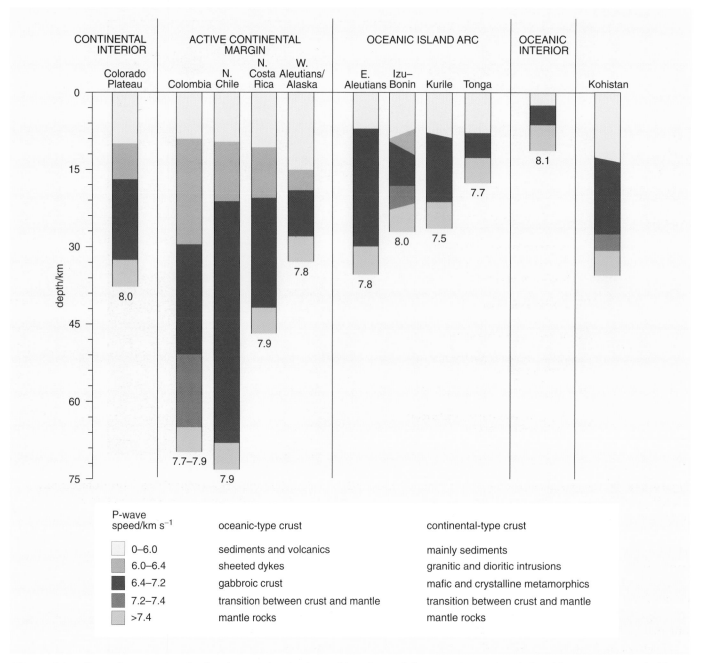

Figure 2.9 Crustal structures of volcanic arcs, the continental interior and the oceanic interior, defined by P-wave speeds (S_P in km s^{-1}). P-wave speeds in the mantle immediately beneath the Moho are given at the bottom of each seismic profile. A section showing lithological layering in the Mesozoic Kohistan arc, exposed in cross-section in Northern Pakistan, is shown for comparison.

The briefest glance at Figure 2.9 might suggest a progression from thin crust in the oceanic interior, through intermediate island arc crust, to thick continental crust. In the broadest sense this reflects the process by which continents accumulate, over many millions of years, by segregation from the mantle. Your answers to Question 2.4 (a) and (b) in turn indicate that subduction-related processes exert a significant influence on crustal structure. Crustal roots below active continental margins can be considerably thicker than those of the continental interior (shield areas). In island arcs, both the upper and lower seismic layers of crust are thicker (by a factor of two to six) than typical ocean crust. The simplest conclusion to draw is that subduction-related processes cause an increase in crustal thickness in the arc region. These processes are examined in subsequent Sections, and include arc magmatism, sediment accretion, and tectonic thickening.

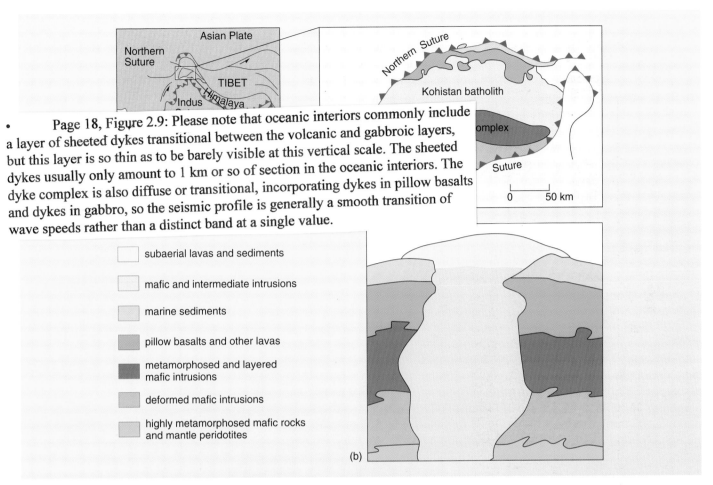

• Page 18, Figure 2.9: Please note that oceanic interiors commonly include a layer of sheeted dykes transitional between the volcanic and gabbroic layers, but this layer is so thin as to be barely visible at this vertical scale. The sheeted dykes usually only amount to 1 km or so of section in the oceanic interiors. The dyke complex is also diffuse or transitional, incorporating dykes in pillow basalts and dykes in gabbro, so the seismic profile is generally a smooth transition of wave speeds rather than a distinct band at a single value.

Figure 2.10 (a) Geological map of the Kohistan arc, northern Pakistan. (b) Schematic cross-section through the Kohistan arc, showing the various components of the mature arc crust as inferred from the tilted stratigraphy seen today. Section is approximately 30 km thick.

Mature island arc crust can reach a thickness of 30 km, approaching the value for some continental regions, while back-arc regions are thinner, comparable to normal oceanic crust. Direct evidence for the crustal thickness of a mature arc comes from estimates of pressure (and thus depth) of high-grade metamorphic rocks from the base of the Kohistan arc, sandwiched between India and Asia during early Tertiary collision. A diagrammatic section through this arc (Figure 2.10) can be constructed because the arc was tilted on its side when the Himalaya were formed. This allows us to compare the geological units with seismic layers in present-day arcs.

- Can the geological layers in Figure 2.10b be assigned to one or other of the seismic layers in Figure 2.9?

- Possibly, yes. Volcanic rocks and sediments make up the upper 12 km or so of the Kohistan arc, a thickness comparable to the upper seismic layer in modern arcs ($S_P = 0$ to $6.0 \ km \ s^{-1}$) in Figure 2.9. The mafic plutonic rocks (e.g. gabbros) and their metamorphic equivalents from 12 to 23 km depth probably correspond to the lower crustal layer in most arcs ($S_P = 6.4$ to $7.2 \ km \ s^{-1}$). Outcrops of highly metamorphosed crystalline rocks mixed with mantle peridotites may represent the transitional zone to the mantle proper ($S_P = 7.2$ to $7.4 \ km \ s^{-1}$) defined in Figure 2.9.

2.2.2 Gravity and heat flow across arc–trench systems

Crustal thickness also varies markedly across the different components of a typical arc system, along with two other important variables — gravity and heat flow — as can be seen on Figure 2.11. Although of normal thickness for oceanic lithosphere, the subducting plate usually defines a slight topographic swell oceanward of the trench; this reflects an elastic flexing of the plate as it subducts. Unlike the subducting oceanic plate, the **fore-arc** region has a crustal thickness intermediate between typical oceanic crust and the arc. This means that the fore-arc region generally has a lower elevation than the arc; indeed, in many cases this region is a submerged basin fed by clastic detritus from the adjacent arc. Vast volumes of sediment can accumulate here, forming piles several kilometres thick. The fore-arc basin is commonly bounded by a low ridge known as the 'fore-arc high' on the oceanward side, formed where incoming material from the subducting plate — both basaltic crust and oceanic sediment — is stacked under the leading edge of the fore-arc. Some of these ridges (e.g. between the Sunda

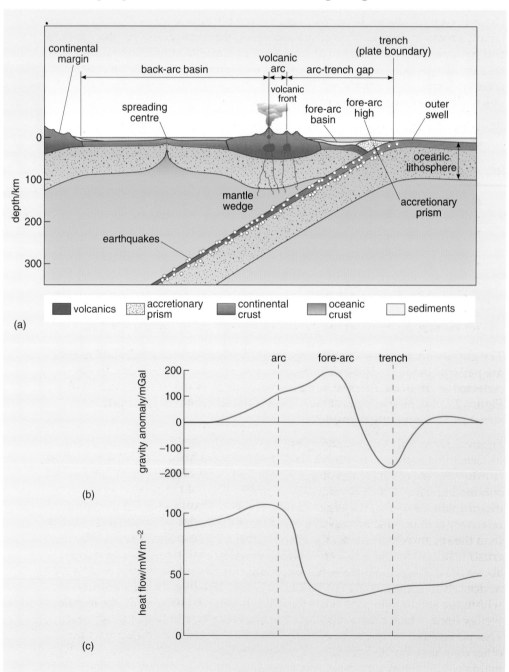

Figure 2.11 Schematic diagrams of the geological and selected geophysical features of subduction zones taken perpendicular to the plate boundary. (a) Cross-section through a destructive plate margin identifying the major geological components and their terminology. (b) Sketch of the free-air gravity anomaly measured across a destructive plate margin. (c) Sketch of the surface heat flow across a destructive plate margin.

trench and Sumatra) rise above sea-level, but Figure 2.11 illustrates the more usual submarine feature. The Mariana trench has very little accumulated sediment, and incidentally contains the deepest point in the oceans, Challenger Deep, at 11 033 m below sea-level. This lack of sediment means that the fore-arc high is composed mainly of basaltic crust, including remnants of seamounts underplated during subduction. Conical mounds of serpentine mud — hydrated mantle peridotite — also occur in the fore-arc region near the trench. They arise from the addition of water to mantle rocks along the subduction zone, forming bodies of serpentine that rise buoyantly through the thin fore-arc crust aided by the presence of extensional faults, and upwell quietly at the surface. Alkaline water-rich fluids (pH > 12) emanating from the same mounds are thought to be sourced from the subducting slab because they contain fragments of metamorphosed basalt.

There is considerable variety in the character of fore-arc regions. The Mariana fore-arc is dominated by oceanic crust, but this includes MORBs and OIBs as well as basalts more typical of island arc settings. The extensional faults that channel serpentinite to the surface also expose ultramafic rocks from the mantle. Japan, a more mature arc, has a fore-arc region that comprises complex igneous and metamorphic basement of at least Paleozoic age. Continental margin fore-arcs are also usually regions of complicated basement rocks, older arcs or accreted terranes. Magmatic activity is rare, however, with minor basaltic volcanism in only a few examples.

- What does the free-air gravity anomaly curve indicate about the isostatic state of the lithosphere in the vicinity of the trench?

- As you saw in Block 1 (Section 1.4.2), deviation of the free-air gravity from zero means that the lithosphere at that point is not in isostatic equilibrium. A positive anomaly implies some upward force, or a subsurface density excess. A negative anomaly reflects a downward force, or low-density material below the surface.

  Question 2.5 From the information given above and your knowledge of Block 1, explain briefly the origin of the following free-air gravity anomalies in the subduction zone system: (a) the pronounced negative anomaly centred on the trench; (b) the marked positive anomaly that peaks over the fore-arc; (c) the minor positive anomaly occurring just oceanward of the trench.

The gravity anomalies shown in Figure 2.11 demonstrate that subduction zones are perhaps the most dynamic part of the plate tectonic system, and this is reflected again in the thermal signature of destructive margins illustrated in Figure 2.11 by the surface heat flow. How does this relate to the thermal structure of the mantle at depth?

Figure 2.12 provides two model perspectives on the thermal structure of two different subduction zones in NE and SW Japan. The lines of equal temperature (**isotherms**) in both localities display a marked depression in the vicinity of the subducting plate, which is a significant perturbation of the normal heat distribution (as seen at the edges of both models). Continuous subduction of relatively cold oceanic lithosphere means that the Wadati–Benioff zone is cooler than the surrounding mantle. By contrast, the arc lithosphere (particularly the crust) is heated by the influx of hot magmas generated in the **mantle wedge** above the downgoing plate — although this elevation of isotherms is not very noticeable in these models. An additional factor affecting the temperatures within the subduction zone is the flow that is assumed to occur in the mantle wedge itself, which draws relatively hot asthenosphere in from further afield. This partially counteracts the cooling effect that the subducting plate would otherwise have on the overriding lithospheric plate where the arc is sited. Two main modes of flow have been recognized:

Corner flow — driven by the viscous drag of the subducting plate on the mantle above, this flow is parallel to the direction of convergence. Mantle material drawn down adjacent to the downgoing plate is replaced by a high-level flow from the back-arc region towards the trench. The white arrows in Figure 2.12 show this corner flow.

Arc-parallel flow — where the flow direction is perpendicular to the convergence direction, i.e. roughly parallel to the length of the arc. This may reflect mantle material being sucked in from either end of the arc system as the subducting slab rolls back oceanwards, retreating from the arc. Examples include the Aleutian and Kurile arcs.

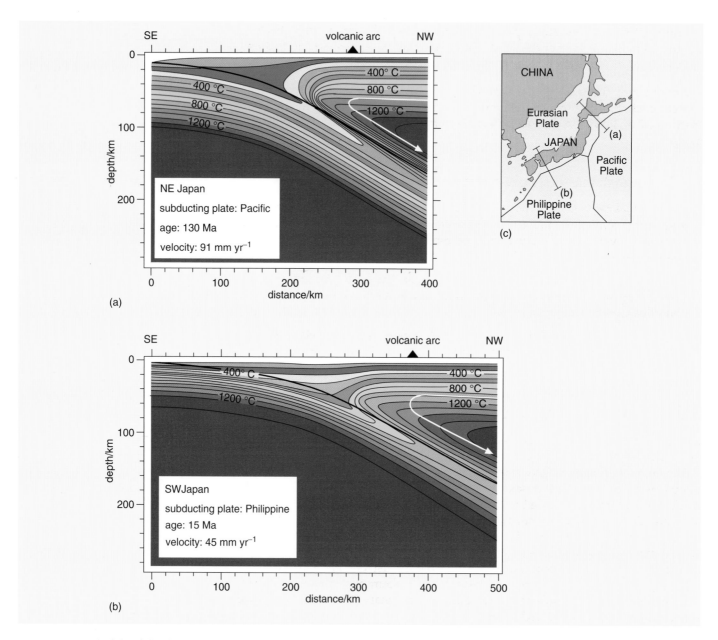

Figure 2.12 Models of the thermal structure of two different sectors of a convergent margin. (a) NE Japan, where the Pacific Plate is subducting beneath the Eurasian margin. (b) SW Japan, where the Philippine Plate is subducting beneath the Eurasian margin. (c) Location map.

● What important principle does the thermal structure depicted in Figure 2.12 highlight?

● Because the uniform increase of temperature with depth (the geotherm) is perturbed in the subduction zone, the rates of both tectonic and magmatic heat transport must be significantly higher than the rate of heat conduction in rocks. For example, the oceanic plate is subducted so rapidly that it does not have time to heat up, even at mantle depths.

Comparing these two subduction zones provides significant insights into the factors influencing the thermal regime of arc–trench systems.

> **Question 2.6** Compare the information given in Figure 2.12 for the two destructive margins, and explain how each of the following factors affects the thermal structure of the subduction zones: (a) the age of the subducting plate; (b) the speed at which the plate subducts.

The contrasting thermal regimes within an arc–trench system have important consequences for both magma generation (Section 3) and metamorphism (Section 6.2.3), leaving a distinctive signature in the rocks of ancient destructive margins.

2.2.3 Summary of Section 2.2

- Crustal thickness varies across a single arc system and between different arcs, with active continental margins having thicker crust than oceanic island arcs. Arcs also develop thicker crust than corresponding 'normal' oceanic or continental crust, indicating that subduction leads to crustal growth.

- The overriding crust nearest the trench is thinner than under the arc, so this fore-arc region is commonly submerged. It may be a sedimentary basin or contain a variety of igneous rocks.

- The downgoing lithospheric slab in the Wadati–Benioff zone is relatively cold, while the mantle wedge and overlying arc are relatively hot regions.

2.3 Accretionary prisms

On the leading edge of the crust overriding the subduction zone, just landward of the trench, there is often a wedge-shaped pile of material, mostly soft sediment, that appears to have been scraped off the downgoing plate. This is known as the **accretionary prism**, or accretionary wedge (Figure 2.11). To avoid confusion with the mantle wedge *beneath* the arc, throughout this Block this accumulation of mostly sedimentary material will be referred to as the accretionary prism, or simply 'the prism'. However, some textbooks and articles contain the equivalent term 'accretionary wedge', and mechanical models of accretionary prism behaviour use 'wedge' almost exclusively, because the wedge shape of the sediment pile is crucial to its mathematical description. This Section describes the various morphologies of accretionary prisms, as well as the main structures associated with them.

2.3.1 Morphology, composition and variation of prisms

Not every destructive plate margin possesses a prism, but of those that do, the prism may be accretionary (prism growing) or non-accretionary (prism shrinking). In fact, about 44% of Earth's aggregate convergent margin length is non-accretionary and about 56% is accretionary (Figure 2.13). Each year, a total of about 1 cubic kilometre of upper plate material returns to the mantle.

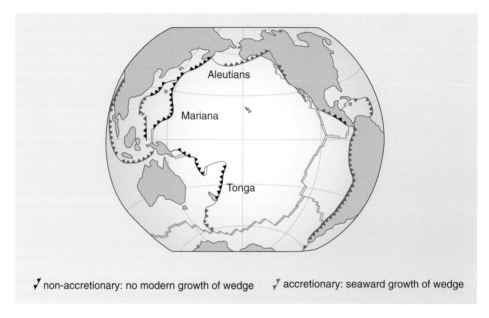

Figure 2.13 Location of accretionary and non-accretionary convergent margins around the Pacific, Caribbean and eastern Indian Ocean. Accretionary margins are defined as those where the volume of accreted material at the plate margin is presently increasing.

The reason why so many convergent margins have at least some accreted material is partly that young pelagic sediment is easily pared off the oceanic plate, and partly because the subduction trench is a natural 'sediment sink' for any detritus eroded off nearby emergent landmasses (e.g. the arc or fore-arc). Sediments from these two different sources — the deep ocean or the arc margin — are of contrasting character. The thin veneer of sediment supplied continuously by the subducting oceanic plate is dominated by fine-grained siliceous or calcareous oozes or clays deposited in deep-sea environments. Rarer limestones indicate deposition in shallower water (e.g. coral atolls atop seamounts), while even rarer coarse clastic sediment (silts and sands) imply sedimentation closer to land (for instance, an oceanic island). In contrast, sediment derived from the overriding plate, usually the magmatic arc or the fore-arc high, is both coarser and more voluminous than the pelagic sediment. This eroded detritus is dominantly clastic material, much of it transported by high-energy density flows plunging down towards the subduction trench. The resulting thick, graded deposits (turbidites) blanket the sea-floor towards the rear of the prism, filling in the many small basins that form on top of the prism (Figure 2.14). Such prism-top sedimentation is supplemented by minor oceanic sediments that drape the upper surface of the accreted material.

Figure 2.15a and b shows a seismic section through the Costa Rica accretionary prism, with a line-drawing interpretation of the overall structure to show the basic components of the sediment pile. Much of the internal prism structure is obscure, reflecting the generally chaotic deformation within the pile of sediment, but the lower boundary with the subducting plate is very sharp. This boundary, termed the **décollement**, is a zone of intense shearing where the strong basalts of the oceanic crust slip under the weak prism sediments. The two systems are generally almost entirely decoupled from each other: very little oceanic sediment is subducted, while only small fragments of basaltic material are ripped up and incorporated into the prism.

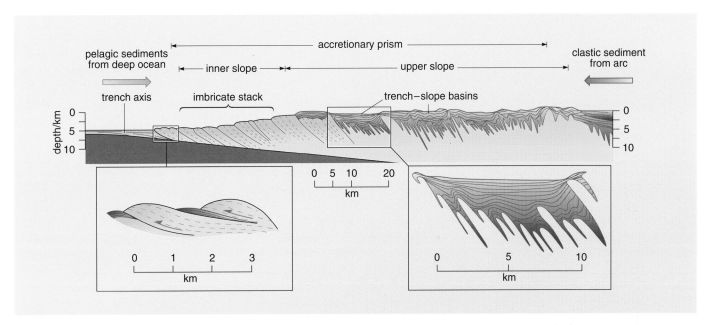

Figure 2.14 Structure of an accretionary prism showing sediment sources and sinks, based on the Sunda fore-arc region, Indonesia. Younger sediments are accreted at the toe (left) on shallow thrust faults. Steeper thrust faults cut older accreted sediments towards the rear of the prism, folding the later sediments deposited in small trench–slope basins on the upper surface of the prism.

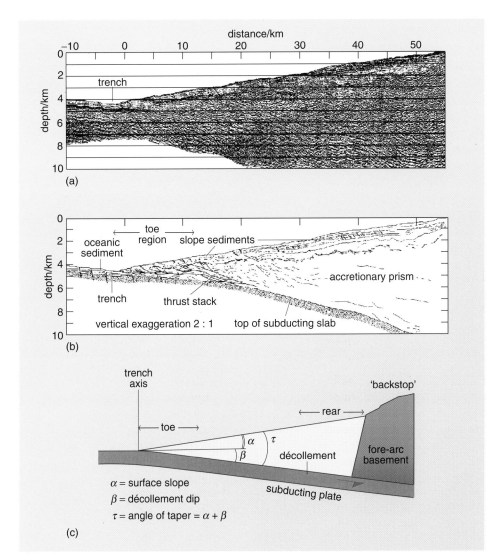

Figure 2.15 (a) Migrated seismic reflection profile of the accretionary prism offshore of Costa Rica. Note the characteristic wedge shape of the sediment pile, tapering towards the trench. (b) Line-drawing interpretation of the seismic profile in (a), picking out the chaotic internal structure draped by slope sediments, and thrust slices of sediment stacked up in the toe region. (c) Cartoon of an accretionary prism, highlighting the main features and their terminology.

There is huge variety in accretionary prisms (Figure 2.16), depending on the sediment supply, convergence rate, duration of subduction, age of oceanic crust and arc proximity, but they all share the basic wedge-shaped geometry (as in Figure 2.15c). This is dictated by the fundamental mechanics of weak material piling up against a rigid 'backstop' (e.g. the arc crust) on a basal shear surface (the décollement). The strength of the prism material influences the **angle of taper** (τ) — the surface slope plus the décollement dip — resulting in the range of tapers shown in Figure 2.16.

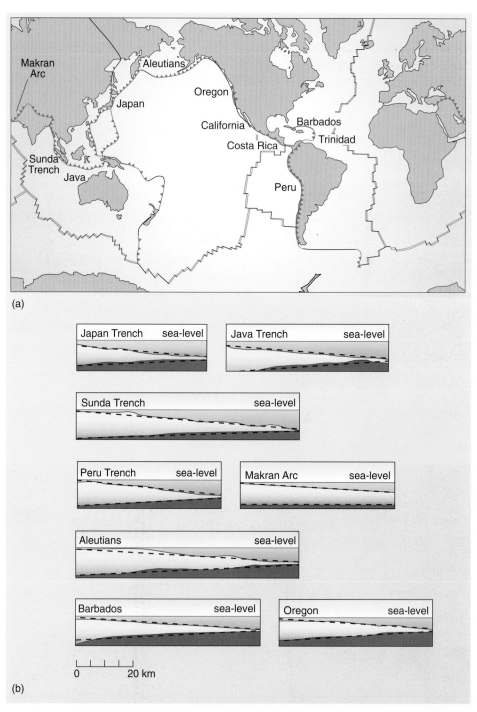

Figure 2.16 (a) Map with locations of the principal accretionary prisms discussed in the text. (b) Sketch cross-sections of several active submarine accretionary prisms, showing their respective angle of taper (surface slope + décollement dip), τ.

● Are all active accretionary prisms submarine features?

● No. While some (e.g. Japan) are submarine, a few emerge above sea-level (e.g. Taiwan, Trinidad), and some have both submerged and emergent portions (e.g. Costa Rica, Barbados, Makran, New Zealand).

It is from the emergent prisms that geologists have garnered much of the information on structures within accretionary prisms.

2.3.2 Structures in accretionary prisms

Accretionary prisms are constantly deforming, developing both **brittle** and **ductile structures** at all levels. **Thrust** (reverse) faults are very common (Figure 2.17a), as might be expected for these dominantly compressional systems. A series of thrust faults together, separating successive thrust sheets, is known as

(a)

(b)

Figure 2.17 Brittle structures in accretionary prisms. (a) Minor thrust in turbiditic sandstones and shales from Japan. Width of view *c.* 1 m. (b) Imbricate stack in a single sandstone layer in turbidites, Makran prism, Pakistan.

an **imbricate stack**. These structures are common at the prism toe (to the left in Figure 2.14), and also at depth as material is underplated to the base of the prism (a small-scale example is shown in Figure 2.17b). Because the prism is so weak, it also deforms in a ductile manner (i.e. by flowing rather than fracturing). This results in folds at all scales, illustrated in Figure 2.18 for the Aleutians, the Makran, and California. These folds are commonly chaotic, betraying both the weakness of the deforming material and the complexity of deformation. Ductile deformation occasionally forms planar fabrics (e.g. **cleavage**) in the rock, where clay minerals are aligned under compression to produce a fabric like the pages of an old book. Such fabrics appear to be rare, perhaps due to the ease with which further deformation can obscure or erase them.

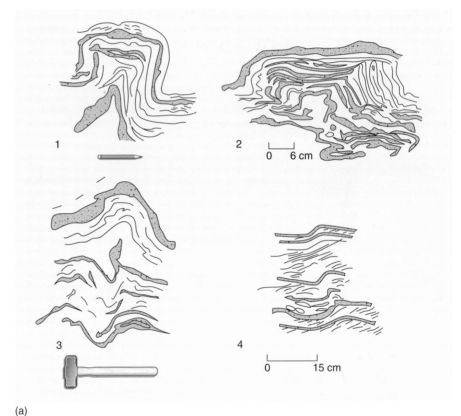

(a)

Figure 2.18 Ductile structures in accretionary prisms. (a) Field sketches of chaotic fold styles in interlayered sandstone and mudrock in the Aleutian fore-arc, Kodiak Island, Alaska. (b) Tight anticline forming a ridge in sediments of the Makran prism, Pakistan. The anticline trends roughly parallel with the plate margin. (c) Tightly folded cherts from an ancient accretionary prism near the Golden Gate Bridge, San Francisco, California.

(b)

(c)

Extensional (normal) faults are also found in accretionary prisms, despite their overall compressional origin. They are generally confined to the upper surface of the prism, towards the rear, and commonly result in small half-graben basins that become infilled with sediment (to the right in Figure 2.14). All the structures above, including the seemingly contradictory extensional faults, are recognized from large-scale collisional mountain belts, explored in Block 4. Indeed, the model of a wedge-shaped mass of material is often used as an analogue for deformation within mountain belts, and we will examine current theories that try to explain structures in prisms further in Section 5.

A final class of structures in accretionary prisms reflects the role of water and other fluids within the prism. Prism sediments are naturally fluid-rich, and high fluid pressure can be generated by dehydration of clay minerals at depth and sediment loading. This pressure is released in a number of ways, forming a range of dewatering structures. These include mineral- or mud-filled veins, and sandstone dykes forcefully injected into more brittle strata. Balloon-shaped bodies of fluidized sediment called diapirs rise buoyantly through the prism. Either dykes or diapirs may reach the surface, where the slurry oozes or even erupts out to form mud volcanoes (Figure 2.19). Such features are often associated with similar effusions of natural gas or liquid hydrocarbons, such as form the tar lakes in Trinidad (Figure 2.20).

(a)

(b)

(c)

(d)

Figure 2.19   (a) Vent of mud volcano, southern Taiwan, with gas bubble. (b) Small mud volcano vent in the Makran prism, showing recent mudflows (dark) oozing over older mudflows (cracked). Two more mud volcanoes stand in the background. (c) First photographed eruption of a mud volcano, Piparo, Trinidad, 22 February 1997. (d) Destructive mudflow from the eruption in (c).

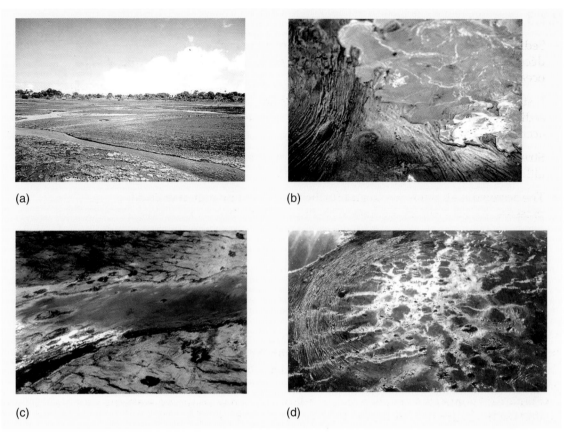

Figure 2.20 (a) General view of La Brea Pitch Lake, Trinidad, with surface water pools and sulphur staining ('Brea' is Spanish for tar). (b) Folds in tar surface and fresh tar seepage, La Brea Pitch Lake, Trinidad. (c) Sulphur rising to surface of La Brea Pitch Lake, Trinidad. Notice tension cracks (dark) in tar. (d) Convection cell on surface of La Brea Pitch Lake, Trinidad.

In Figure 2.15, the internal structure of the Costa Rica prism on the seismic section seemed very chaotic. Is there any geological evidence in emergent prisms that is consistent with this? In many ancient accretionary prisms, such as the Franciscan Complex in California that you will study in Section 6, there are large tracts of chaotic deposits, consisting of a disrupted matrix of either clay or serpentinite peppered with blocks of other sediments, basalts, metamorphosed oceanic crust, and even mantle rocks. These deposits are known as **mélanges** (from the French for 'mixture'), and they are commonly associated with accretionary prisms. When chaotic deposits like these are composed entirely of sedimentary rocks — for instance, rafts and blocks of stronger rock (sandstone or limestone) in a disrupted matrix of mudrock — they are known as **olistostromes** (from the Greek *olistos* = sliding and *stroma* = bed). Although such sedimentary deposits occur in a range of environments besides accretionary complexes, they are one of the key pieces of evidence in recognizing ancient accretionary prisms and, therefore, ancient convergent plate margins.

2.3.3 Summary of Section 2.3

- Sedimentary material accumulates at an accreting margin above a décollement surface that dips beneath the fore-arc. The sediments may be of oceanic or continental derivation.

- Just over half the world's convergent margins are currently accreting sedimentary material into prisms at oceanic trenches; the rest are non-accretionary.

- Structures observed in accretionary prisms are mainly compressional, although some extensional features also occur.

- The accreted material is weak, and further weakened by high pore fluid pressure in the prism, giving rise to chaotic internal structure.

2.4 Volcanoes and magmatism

2.4.1 Volcanic arcs

Most of the Earth's active volcanoes on land are found at subduction zones, where they are arranged in long chains lying parallel with the plate boundary, a pattern that is clearly evident on maps such as *'This Dynamic Planet'* (DP). Typically, the arc has a well-defined row of prominent volcanoes, known as the **volcanic front**, a few hundred kilometres from the plate boundary, with a few volcanoes scattered behind the front such that the arc can be over 100 km wide (Figure 2.21).

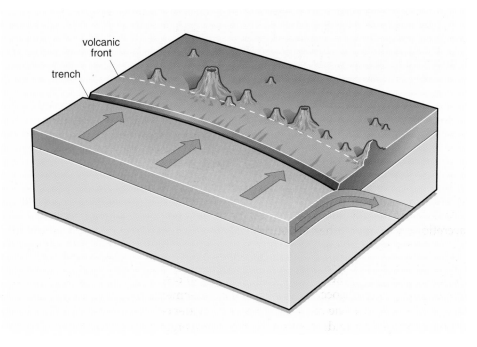

Figure 2.21 Block diagram showing a volcanic arc and its relationship to the plate boundary.

Is there any pattern to the location of the volcanoes that might help explain their occurrence?

● What information could be used to look for useful patterns in the location of volcanoes in arcs?

● The distances between the volcanoes themselves, and distances between the volcanoes and the subducting plate, might be significant. This requires us to assess information on the spacing of volcanoes, the distance from the plate boundary to the volcanic front, and the vertical distance between the volcanoes and the subducting slab.

The spacing between volcanoes varies from arc to arc. For instance, in the Central American arc, the average spacing is 24 km. At the other extreme, active volcanoes in the Izu–Bonin and Mariana arcs (western Pacific) are spaced much more widely, at about 75 km. These spacings probably reflect the distances between crustal weaknesses exploited by rising magma.

Now consider the broader plate tectonic geometry by answering the following question, based on Figure 2.22.

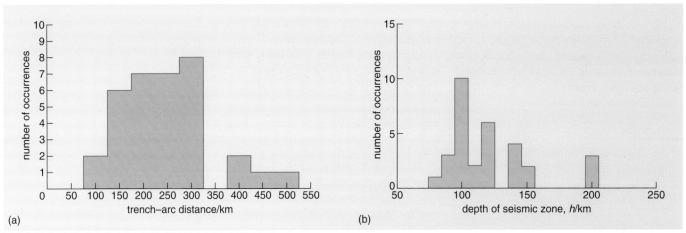

Figure 2.22 (a) Histogram of distance between trench and volcanic front. (b) Histogram of vertical distance between the volcanic front and the top of the Wadati–Benioff zone.

Question 2.7 Briefly describe the variation in arc–trench gap and slab depth. How broad is the variation in each of these distances?

The average slab depth is close to 110 km, with the depth for well over half of the arcs being within ±20 km of this value. Such a narrow range of slab depths is quite remarkable, especially given that the uncertainty in locating the top of the slab from earthquake foci must be a few kilometres at least. That the volcanic front is consistently situated in such a precise location above the subducting slab suggests that the processes by which the magmas are generated depend on depth, and hence pressure. We will return to this after collecting some further geological and geochemical evidence to bring to the discussion.

2.4.2 Santorini, a subduction zone volcano

Santorini volcano, in the Aegean Sea, is a Greek island with a long history of archaeological and geological investigation. It is part of the Aegean subduction system. At this point in Block 3, Santorini provides a useful introduction to the types of volcanic rocks and eruption styles that are found at subduction zones. Later in the Block, you will use data and other observations from Santorini to explore the processes by which arc magmas evolve underground, prior to eruption.

To set the scene, Figure 2.23a locates the island volcanoes of the Aegean Arc, which lies about 250 km north of the Hellenic Trench where the African Plate starts to descend beneath the Eurasian Plate (DP and Figure 2.1). The trench marks the southern edge of the Aegean microplate, which abuts the Eurasian Plate proper along transform faults in northern Greece and Turkey. Earthquake foci define a Wadati–Benioff zone, which dips north of the trench and lies 150 km beneath the active volcanic front. The present arc is about 4 million years old and subduction is believed to have started 13 to 16 million years ago. Santorini has been active for 650 000 years, is currently the most active volcano in the arc and last erupted in 1950.

Santorini comprises a group of islands forming a broken ring about 15 km across, with two islands at the centre of the ring (Figure 2.23b overleaf). The oldest rocks on Santorini are Tertiary schists and Triassic marbles, forming the basement on which the volcano is built. The volcanic rocks are a mixture of lava flows and pyroclastic units. Much of Santorini's surface is covered by layers of

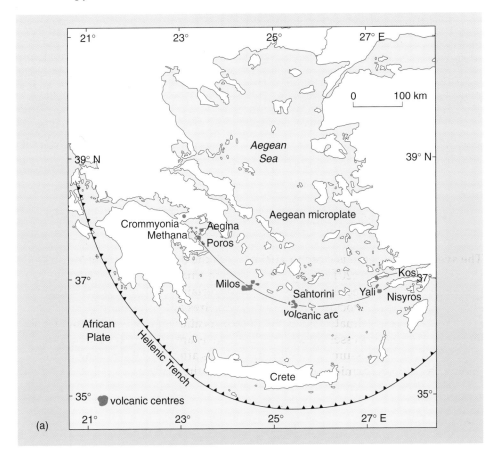

Figure 2.23 (a) Map showing the location of volcanoes within the Aegean arc.
(b) Overleaf: Map of the Santorini island group.

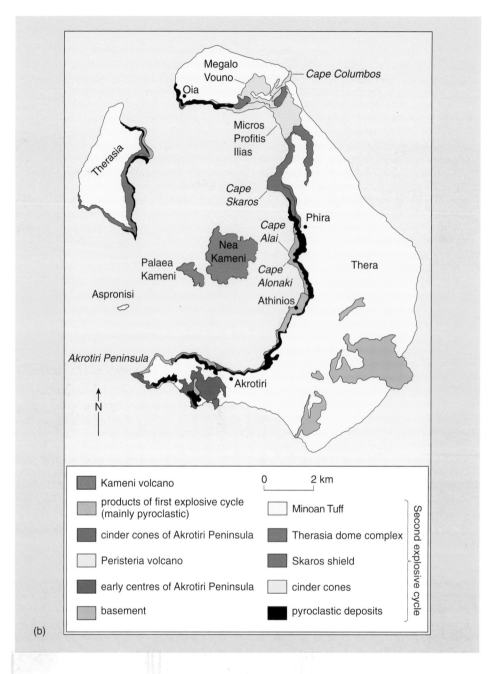

(b)

white pumice up to several metres thick produced during the last major eruption. Dated at about 1627 BC, this event is known as the Minoan eruption because it is closely linked in time with the demise of the Minoan civilization that was based in Crete, 100 km to the south. The deposits from this devastating eruption include airfall (plinian) deposits and various pyroclastic flow deposits collectively known as the Minoan Tuff. The volume of magma erupted was so large (recent estimates vary from about 30 km^3 to as high as 70 km^3) that the surface of the volcano fell in, with the roof of the magma chamber collapsing into the drained chamber to form a **caldera**. So, the outer slopes of Santorini are the gently dipping flanks of a volcano whereas the inner shores are steep cliffs that formed when the caldera collapsed. A view from the caldera rim (Figure 2.24a) shows impressive cross-sections through the volcanic sequence in the caldera walls.

(a)

(b)

(c)

Figure 2.24 (a) Northward view of the eastern caldera wall and rim, Santorini. The gently sloping flanks of the volcano dip to the right (east). In the foreground, the pale rocks are pumiceous airfall and pyroclastic flow deposits of the Minoan eruption. Beneath them are exposed older lava flows. The cliffs are about 250 m high. (b) View of some 30 lava flows in the Skaros cliffs north of Phira. (c) View of Nea Kameni from the cliffs on the eastern side of the caldera. Lavas of different ages are identifiable on the basis of differing degrees of weathering and vegetation. The southern tip of Therasia, on the western side of the caldera, and Aspronisi can be seen in the background.

By carefully mapping the rocks exposed in the cliffs, geologists have reconstructed the sequence of volcanic activity. Many lava flows a few metres thick are present in some areas (Figures 2.23b and 2.24b) such that distinct centres of lava eruption have been identified. Eruptions from the oldest centre built a 2 km³ composite cone known as Peristeria. Layers of lava also form the volcanic centres of Therasia and Skaros distinguished on the geological map, but large parts of these volcanic centres were destroyed by caldera collapse, with four collapses recognized in the volcano's stratigraphy. The most recent caldera collapse was associated with the Minoan eruption and brought to an end the second of two 'explosive cycles' that comprise most of Santorini's volcanic history.

After the Minoan eruption, the volcano started to grow again in a series of lava eruptions. These built the two small islands of Palaea Kameni and Nea Kameni (translated as old and new smoking islands, respectively) which are shown in Figures 2.23b and 2.24c. The oldest exposed lava dates from 197 BC and the youngest from 1950 AD.

While Santorini is just one example of a subduction zone volcano, it is fairly representative in that it has evolved through stages of lava eruptions and pyroclastic eruptions. In the case of Santorini, the volume erupted in some eruptions has been so large as to cause caldera collapse when the roof of the evacuated magma storage region (a magma chamber) foundered. Cycles of growth and destruction, on time-scales of many tens to hundreds of thousands of years, are the typical 'lifestyle' of many subduction zone volcanoes.

2.4.3 Magma types

Subduction zone volcanoes show a range of eruption styles, as the example of Santorini demonstrates, but what are the chemical compositions of their magmas, and how do they compare with those of other plate tectonic settings? In Section 2.2.3 of Block 2, the total alkalis against silica diagram for the chemical classification of igneous rocks was introduced. This diagram is shown again in Figure 2.25, but this time with volcanic rocks from Santorini plotted on it as an example of a subduction zone volcano.

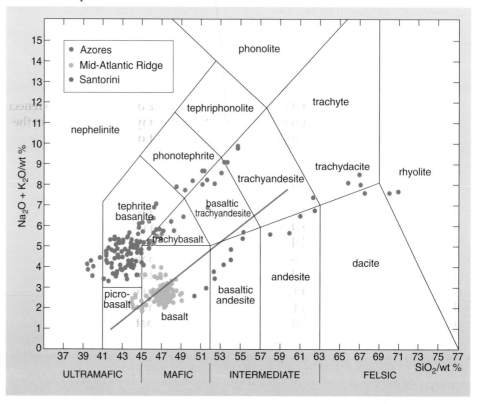

Figure 2.25 Plot of total alkalis (Na₂O + K₂O) against silica (SiO₂) showing fields of different rock names (cf. Block 2, Figure 2.2), and data for volcanic rocks from Santorini, the Azores (a hot spot in the Atlantic Ocean) and the Mid-Atlantic Ridge. The red line separates alkaline from sub-alkaline compositions (Block 2, Figure 2.3).

● According to the classification scheme of Figure 2.25, what igneous rock types are present on Santorini?

● The data points fall in the fields of basalt, basaltic andesite, andesite, trachyandesite, trachydacite, dacite and rhyolite.

Had we chosen to plot volcanic rocks from other subduction zones (such as the Mariana island arc of the western Pacific; see Block 2, Figure 2.4), the data would plot in the same range of 'boxes', although the particular points might not have overlapped precisely. Usually, the volcanic rocks from subduction zones have sufficiently low alkali contents that they do not encroach into the trachyandesite or trachydacite fields, and this tectonic setting is dominated by a **basalt–andesite–dacite association**.

The rock name andesite is significant here! The Andes of South America are part of a major subduction zone and have over 150 active volcanoes. When the area was explored by Europeans at the end of the 18th century, they found volcanic rocks unlike those familiar to them from Iceland, Vesuvius or Etna. The new rock warranted a new name, and the term andesite was born. Subsequent studies have found that many arc volcanoes contain andesite in abundance.

The comparison between the chemical compositions of the volcanic rocks from Santorini and other tectonic settings in Figure 2.25 reveals two distinctive features of subduction zone magmas. First, a range of silica content is present (unlike mid-ocean ridges where basalt is almost exclusively found). Secondly, the amount of total alkalis is less (at a given SiO_2 content) than in many hot spots, such as the Azores (Block 2, Figure 2.4), and continental rifts such as Kenya (Block 2, Figure 3.6). Whereas magmas from the latter two examples are classed as alkaline, Santorini in common with most volcanoes in subduction zones is classed as sub-alkaline.

● What factors might be responsible for subduction zone magmas having (i) a wide range of silica contents, and (ii) relatively low alkali contents?

● (i) On the Earth, virtually all igneous activity stems from partial melting of the mantle, which produces basalt. Magmas with higher silica contents than basalt are produced by processes such as fractional crystallization of basalt or partial melting of crustal rocks due to heating by basalt. These processes that modify basalt must be prevalent in subduction zones. (ii) The composition of magmas that are produced by partial melting of mantle peridotite is controlled by the composition of the peridotite and the amount of partial melting, which in turn depends on pressure and temperature. So, the relatively low alkali content of most subduction zone basalts is likely to reflect the composition of the source materials and/or the physical conditions in the regions of partial melting within the roots of subduction zone volcanoes.

2.4.4 Water and other dissolved gases

Subduction zone volcanoes are notorious for being among the world's most destructive. A roll-call of recent deadly eruptions — Pinatubo in 1991 (Philippines), Ruiz in 1985 (Colombia), Mount St Helens in 1980 (USA), Krakatau in 1883 (Indonesia) — amounts to a list of famous explosive eruptions at subduction zone volcanoes. Santorini's Minoan eruption may have been responsible for ending Minoan civilization. The high explosivity of these volcanoes is related to the relatively high gas content and a high viscosity of the magmas. The combination of these two factors means that when the magma approaches the surface, gas exsolves from it and expands rapidly with falling pressure, causing the sticky liquid to be torn apart. What starts as the slow rise of viscous magma to the surface can end in the emission of volcanic gas and pumice at very high speeds into the atmosphere, as the cover photograph of an eruption of the Soufrière Hills volcano, Montserrat, shows.

Because gases are lost from magmas when they erupt, a chemical analysis of a volcanic rock cannot provide information about the amounts of water and other gases dissolved in magmas at depth. One clue to the original water content is that some dacites and rhyolites from subduction zones contain phenocrysts of amphibole and sometimes biotite. The significance of this simple observation is that these two minerals contain water in their structure, so the magma from which they crystallized must also have contained water. Experiments have shown that more than about 4% water is needed before amphibole will crystallize from a liquid of dacitic composition.

Another approach is to analyse small inclusions of glass contained inside phenocrysts (Figure 2.26). The inclusions are tiny samples of liquid that became trapped in the phenocryst as it grew in the magma chamber beneath a volcano. On eruption, the inclusions are quenched to a glass but do not lose any of their dissolved gases because the enclosing crystal acts as a robust container. Analysis of water (H_2O) and chlorine (Cl) in basaltic glasses from a mid-ocean ridge and a subduction zone volcano are shown in Figure 2.27.

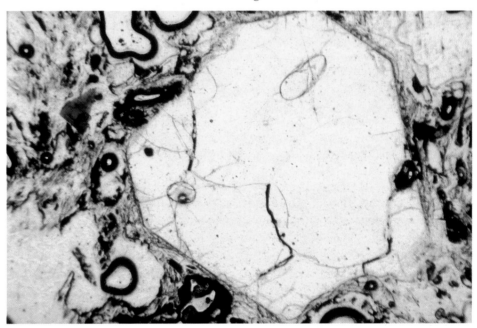

Figure 2.26 Photomicrograph of round glass inclusions in a crystal of quartz. The glass in the inclusion retains a high water content whereas the glass surrounding the crystal vesiculated and degassed during the eruption. Field of view is 1 mm across.

Figure 2.27 A plot of the pre-eruptive water versus chlorine contents of basalts from the North Atlantic mid-ocean ridge and Fuego volcano (Guatemala) in the Central American arc. Mid-Atlantic Ridge data are from basalt glasses quenched by eruption onto the sea-floor under sufficiently high hydrostatic pressure that no gases were lost. Fuego data are from glass inclusions that are assumed to sample the magma in the volcano's magma chamber, prior to eruption.

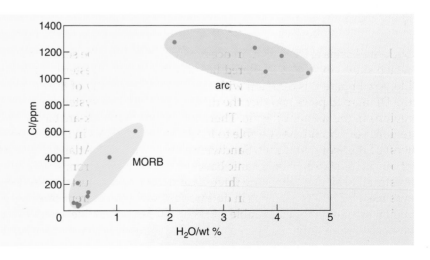

⬤ Compare and contrast the water and chlorine contents of basalt magmas from the Mid-Atlantic Ridge and Fuego volcano.

⬤ The arc basalts have higher water and chlorine contents. Specifically, the plotted data show less than 1% water in all but one of the MORB samples but more than 2% water in all of the arc samples. Chlorine is less than 600 ppm in the MORB samples, but between 1000 and 1300 ppm in the arc samples.

In general, subduction zone magmas are 'wetter' than those from other tectonic settings. One important result of this is that subduction zone volcanoes provide a significant source of atmospheric gases. For example, it has been estimated that, on average, subduction zone volcanoes introduce 10^{10} kg of S, 10^9 to 10^{11} kg Cl, and 10^7 kg of C to the atmosphere each year (mainly as SO_2, HCl and CO_2 respectively).

2.4.5 Summary of Section 2.4

• Volcanoes at subduction zones form arcs with a well-defined front on the side facing the subducting plate. The volcanic front is situated about 110 km above the subducting slab.

• Arc volcanoes produce lava flows and voluminous pyroclastic deposits. In some cases, their growth can be punctuated by caldera collapse.

• Arc volcanoes erupt a range of magma compositions, forming a basalt–andesite–dacite association. The magmas are distinctive in containing more water, and therefore often erupting more explosively, than magmas from other plate tectonic settings.

2.5 Back-arc regions

Behind many arc–trench systems, i.e. lying above the subducting slab on the concave side of the arc, is a region that typically has lower elevation than the arc itself, forming a basin. These regions are therefore most often referred to as **back-arc basins** (Figure 2.11). As is the case in most basins, the crust in this area is being extended. There is considerable variety in these areas however, not least the fundamental division between those occurring within oceanic crust and those underlain by continental crust. This Section examines these two types in turn, focusing on the oceanic case first.

2.5.1 Oceanic back-arc basins

Back-arc basins are common in oceanic settings, as can be seen in Figure 2.28, which shows examples scattered liberally around the western Pacific. You might like to compare this diagram with the actual topography of the ocean floor on the DP map to piece together the different arcs, trench systems and back-arc regions in the western Pacific. There is a plethora of back-arc basins in this region; you should also be able to locate other examples in the Caribbean and west of the Scotia (or South Sandwich) arc in the South Atlantic. However, much of our understanding of oceanic back-arc basins comes from studies in the western Pacific, on which the three-way classification illustrated in Figure 2.28 was based. The criteria used in defining these three different classes of back-arc region are summarized in Table 2.2; they are termed 'active' or 'inactive' with respect to seismicity.

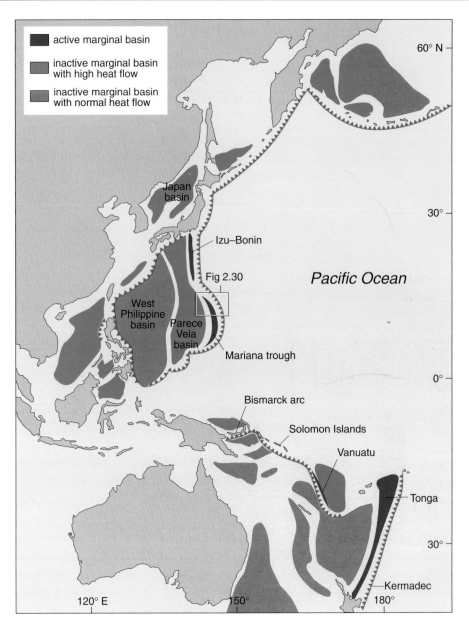

Figure 2.28 Back-arc regions in the western Pacific divided into three principal classes (see key) according to seismicity and heat flow.

Table 2.2 Characteristics of the three different classes of oceanic back-arc basin.

Active	Inactive (hot)	Inactive (cool)
young, newly formed lithosphere	old lithosphere	old lithosphere
high heat flow	high heat flow	low heat flow
seismically active	low seismicity	low seismicity
adjacent to arc	some distance from arc	some distance from arc
active spreading centre common	no active centre, but spreading in past	no active spreading
slow shear wave speeds: partial melting in upper mantle	little or no evidence for partial melting in upper mantle	no evidence for partial melting in upper mantle

The active and inactive (hot) types involve some sort of sea-floor spreading that can be classed as either ordered, disordered or diffuse according to the bathymetric form of the basin (Figure 2.29). Seismic tomography studies have

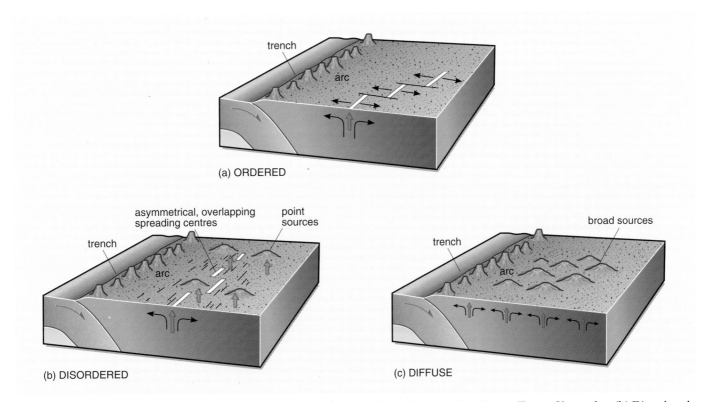

Figure 2.29 Three different modes of back-arc spreading. (a) Ordered: e.g. Mariana, Izu–Bonin, Tonga–Kermadec. (b) Disordered: e.g. Vanuatu, Solomon Islands, Bismarck Arc. (c) Diffuse: e.g. Sea of Japan.

shown that some active back-arc regions, such as the Lau Basin between Tonga and Fiji (Figure 2.6), are underlain by mantle with anomalously low seismic wave speeds (implying warm, buoyant asthenosphere).

> **Question 2.8** (a) Which of the three types of back-arc spreading illustrated in Figure 2.29 is the most similar to a mid-ocean ridge? (b) For each of the other two types of back-arc spreading, describe the differences between their mode of spreading and that of a typical mid-ocean ridge. (c) Do you think the nature of back-arc spreading regions makes them easier to identify than mid-ocean ridges?

Your study of Figure 2.29 should have convinced you that there is a whole spectrum of back-arc regions, ranging from those fairly similar to mid-ocean ridges to ones that are very different. We have now reached the point where we can consider how these regions formed, and why they possess the distinctive features outlined in Table 2.2 and Figure 2.29. Do all back-arc regions share the same origin? In fact, the current consensus is that the active and inactive types of back-arc region have fundamentally different origins, which can be classified thus:

Inactive back-arcs: Entrapment of pre-existing oceanic lithosphere.

Active back-arcs: Generation of new oceanic lithosphere.

Inactive back-arcs are thought to form by entrapment of an area of oceanic lithosphere during an episode of tectonic reconfiguration. This might occur when subduction switches direction, or 'jumps' from one location to another, isolating a piece of ocean floor.

Active back-arcs, whether ordered, disordered or diffuse, owe their existence to partial melting in the mantle and the formation of new crust. Most active back-arc basins share one distinctive feature that provides a clue to their formation. This is known as the remnant arc, and is an arcuate ridge of volcanic rock with arc affinities. Examples include the Aves Ridge in the Caribbean, and the West

Mariana Ridge in the western Pacific (Figure 2.30). Some basic observations on these remnant arcs are:

- The remnant arc is older than most of the rocks on the adjacent, active arc.

- The remnant arc is older than the oceanic crust of the back-arc basin that separates the remnant arc from the active arc.

- Sediments in the back-arc basin are generally both thinner, and younger, than those on the opposite sides of the remnant arc or the active arc.

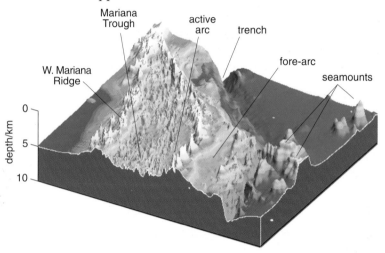

Figure 2.30 Exaggerated perspective view of the northern end of the Mariana Arc and back-arc basin, with the West Mariana Ridge (remnant arc) diverging from the current arc. Location of view is given by box on Figure 2.28.

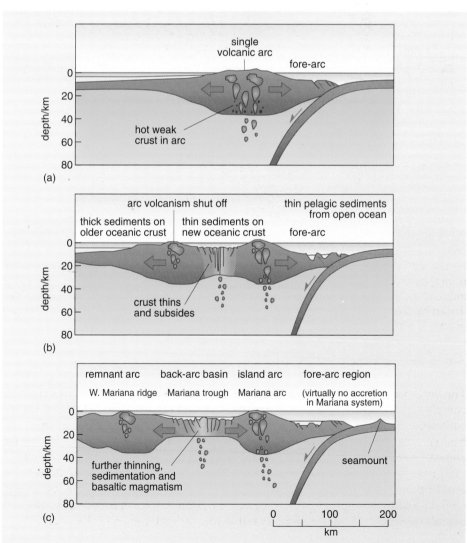

Figure 2.31 Cartoon illustrating the sequence of events (a), (b) and (c) in a model for the formation of an active back-arc basin by arc splitting. The model has been derived with the Mariana subduction zone in mind.

These observations led to the basic theory for the formation of an active back-arc, summarized in Figure 2.31, which suggests that a pre-existing arc split down the middle. New oceanic crust was formed in the resulting spreading centre, and the two halves of the arc gradually separated. One half (the remnant arc) became inactive, while the other experienced continuing magmatism, remaining an active arc.

● Casting your mind back to Block 1, what property of the original arc crust might favour splitting there rather than somewhere else in the region?

● The arc crust has an elevated geotherm and, being hot, is therefore relatively weak. This zone of weakness will tend to be exploited first if tectonic forces put the region under tension, with ductile deformation acting to thin the crust until a spreading centre is formed, as Figure 2.31 illustrates.

There is no consensus yet on the driving force causing back-arc spreading itself, and some alternative theories are compared in Figure 2.32. Current theories on melting processes in the mantle wedge are at odds with the scenario depicted in Figure 2.32a, and would favour either (b) or (c). Many workers believe that **trench suction** (Block 1, Section 1.3) initiates extension in the overriding plate, which is then further weakened by the ascent of magma from the mantle.

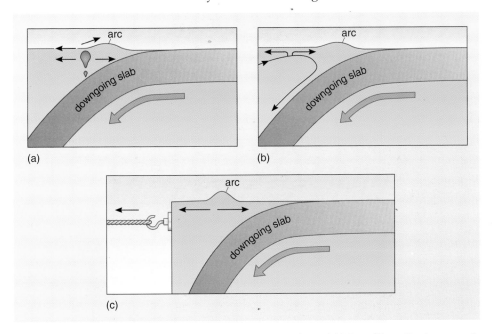

Figure 2.32 Theories for the causes of back-arc spreading. (a) Upwelling diapir sourced from the downgoing slab weakens overlying crust and initiates spreading. (b) Spreading induced in the overriding plate by viscous drag due to corner flow in the mantle wedge, driven by the motion of the subducting slab. (c) Spreading induced by the relative retreat of the overriding plate from the downgoing slab.

2.5.2 Continental back-arc regions

The back-arc regions of continental areas are much less distinct, and much more complex, than their oceanic counterparts because they occur in heterogeneous continental crust. Although extension in the back-arc region may produce basinal areas, these are rarely marine. One exception is the Central Andes, where ancient marine back-arc basins dating from a time when the active continental margin was a less mature arc feature have been caught up in the mountain-building processes, and these are discussed further in Section 7. Earthquake and GPS data indicate that the present back-arc regions of South America are in overall compression, an unusual situation for the back-arc crust. This has resulted in the formation of linear fold and thrust belts such as the sub-Andean ranges to the east of the widest part of the Andes (Figure 2.33a). Compression in the overriding plate is due to its advance over the trench, compounded by shallow subduction dips. The extensional Altiplano plateau between the active arc and the sub-Andean ranges is thus unlikely to reflect trench suction or retreat, as in oceanic settings. It is probably related more to the response of thickened crust to changes in the underlying mantle, processes addressed in Block 4 for the evolution of the Tibetan plateau.

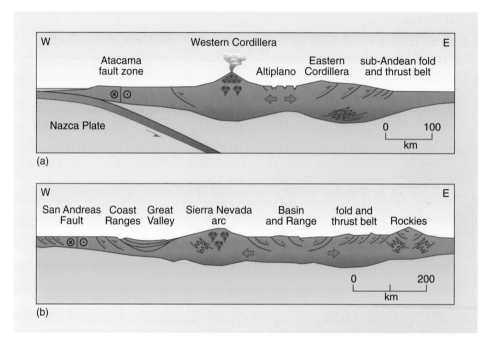

Figure 2.33 (a) Schematic cross-section through the Central Andes, showing the Altiplano plateau and the sub-Andean fold and thrust belt in the back-arc region. (b) Cartoon to illustrate a model for the formation of the extensional Basin and Range Province in the western United States.

In North America, by contrast, there is a vast extensional area of the mid-west known as the Basin and Range (Block 1, Activity 3.1), riddled with basins including the famous Death Valley (90 m below sea-level), which represents the back-arc region to the long-lived continental arcs of western North America (Figure 2.33b). Until the Miocene, this area was a compressional back-arc, similar to the sub-Andean ranges in South America and the Rockies to the north. Since then, although active subduction has ceased along the continental margin at these latitudes, some form of back-arc extension has produced a region of thin crust (20–25 km) and high heat flow. As with the Altiplano, however, there are conflicting views as to the cause of the shift from compression to extension. Current theories again appeal to a change from shallow subduction to a steep slab, with some researchers suggesting break-off of part of the slab, or an additional input of heat from the subducted East Pacific Rise. Such heat input would result in uplift and lithospheric weakening, followed by extension and subsidence.

2.5.3 Summary of Section 2.5

• Back-arc regions in both oceanic and continental settings are commonly extensional, basinal areas; the Andean back-arc is the main compressional example.

• Some oceanic back-arcs contain active spreading centres generating new crust, formed by splitting of an earlier volcanic arc.

Objectives for Section 2

Now that you have completed this Section, you should be able to:

2.1 Understand the meaning of all the terms printed in **bold**.

2.2 Outline the variation in the overall form and nature of subduction zones and their associated features, and explain the reasons behind that variation.

2.3 Place the fundamental processes of subduction zones in a plate tectonic context.

2.4 Summarize the rates at which subduction zone processes occur, and the typical life-span of a single subduction zone.

2.5 Describe the lithosphere in the vicinity of a subduction zone in terms of its general dimensions, and its thermal and mechanical properties.

2.6 Describe the basic components of an arc–trench system, including the fore-arc, accretionary prisms, volcanic front, and back-arc regions.

2.7 Describe the composition of volcanic rocks from subduction zones and how they differ from lavas from other tectonic settings.

2.8 Describe the processes involved in the formation of accretionary prisms and both oceanic and continental back-arc regions.

3   Magma generation in subduction zones

When plate tectonics was first discussed in the late 1960s and early 1970s, Earth scientists raised the possibility that the descending slab could melt and supply magmas to subduction zone volcanoes. This seemed a reasonable proposition because subduction involves cold lithosphere descending into much hotter mantle, with the expectation that the slab will heat up. And when substances are heated, melting can occur. However, geologists now widely accept that magmatism at subduction zones is caused by partial melting of the mantle. There are many reasons for reaching this conclusion, and some are to do with showing that mantle melting can produce the observed types of magma while other arguments are to do with showing that alternative hypotheses are inconsistent with observations. What lines of evidence lead geologists to accept mantle melting but reject slab melting? In Block 2, insights on the location and cause of magma generation came from two broad areas — subsurface geophysical anomalies and the geochemistry of the erupted magmas.

3.1   Geophysical information

Partial melting causes changes to the density and elastic properties of rock materials, such that their seismic wave speeds change. Consequently, a map or cross-section of the Earth showing the locations of seismic wave speed anomalies can reveal zones of anomalously hot or partially molten rocks. This technique of seismic tomography was one way in which the magma generation zones in the mantle beneath the Kenya Rift were recognized (Block 2, pp. 55–57). Japanese seismologists have developed similar approaches to study the subduction zone in NE Japan, and a typical set of their results is shown in Figure 3.1.

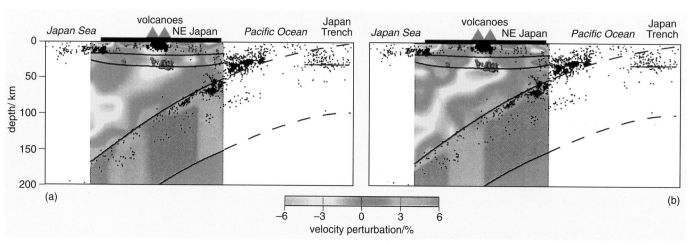

Figure 3.1   Cross-sections perpendicular to the volcanic front in NE Japan, at about 39° 50′ N running westward from the Japan Trench, showing (a) P-wave and (b) S-wave speed anomalies. Red and blue colours represent low and high speeds respectively. Dots represent earthquake foci. Black lines below Japan represent seismic discontinuities and are, in order of increasing depth, the Conrad discontinuity (upper/lower crust interface), Moho, top and base of slab. Note that the vertical bands of pale and dark blue in the slab are artefacts of the computational methods used for data processing rather than real properties.

The earthquake foci in the slab, arc crust and fore-arc crust are prominent in Figure 3.1 and define the familiar distribution of seismicity found at subduction zones. The pattern of velocity anomalies shows regions of reduced wave speeds within the mantle, whereas the slab is fairly homogeneous. The lowered P- and S-wave speeds are explained by the presence of distributed melt (or fluid) pockets, so the cross-section of seismic speed anomalies implies that there is a partially molten region within the mantle wedge lying roughly parallel with the dipping slab. A low-speed anomaly also penetrates the crust directly below the volcanic arc.

3.2 Geochemistry of arc magmas

The two candidate magma sources in subduction zones — the mantle wedge and the subducted slab — have different chemical compositions, so any magmas produced by partial melting of these different materials would be expected to have distinct chemical compositions.

3.2.1 Composition of primitive magmas

In volcanic arcs, the erupted magmas have a range of chemical compositions: the basalt–andesite–dacite association noted in Section 2.4.3. The more evolved magmas are the products of fractional crystallization and other processes that modify the composition of the original, primary magma, so the most primitive compositions will be closest to the primary composition. The primary magma carries the most direct chemical signature of the magma source and melting conditions.

The upper mantle is composed of peridotite, and partial melting of mantle peridotite yields liquids with basaltic compositions and Mg-numbers in the range 65 to 73 (Block 2, p. 31). On the other hand, the uppermost parts of subducted oceanic lithosphere comprise hydrothermally altered MORB, deep-sea sediment and continental sediment, so these materials are the first to heat up as the slab sinks into the mantle. Experiments in which hydrated mid-ocean ridge basalt is heated at high pressure produce partial melting, but with liquids having Mg-numbers in the range 25 to 45, and with SiO_2 contents between 55 and 70%. So, if arc magmas are generated by partial melting of the slab, we would not expect to find basalts or rocks with Mg-numbers much above 45.

> **Question 3.1** What is the Mg-number of a Santorini basalt lava with 50.8% SiO_2, 8.3% FeO and 6.4% MgO?
> [From Block 2, Mg-number $= 100 \times (MgO/40)/((MgO/40) + (FeO/72))$.]

The relatively low silica content and high Mg-number of the Santorini basalt cannot have originated by melting of the subducted slab. This result is repeated throughout the world's subduction zones — most arcs erupt at least some lavas with compositions that are too primitive to have been generated by partial melting of subducted basalt. Although igneous rocks with higher silica contents are erupted (Figure 2.25 shows that they are common), the important point is that the composition of the *most primitive* magmas at arc volcanoes, those which are generally considered to give rise to the more evolved magmas, is not consistent with slab melting.

3.2.2 Trace element patterns of arc basalts

A major conclusion in Block 2 was that the trace element pattern of primitive basalts reflects the trace element pattern of the magmas' mantle source and the degree and depth of partial melting. In Block 2 (Section 2.6), the different trace element patterns of MORB and OIB were explained in terms of different source compositions and different partial melting regimes, so can the trace element patterns of arc basalts reveal something about their source regions? Because oceanic island arcs are sites where subduction zone magmatism proceeds unaffected by thick, cold and compositionally distinct continental lithosphere, they provide the best comparison with basalts from other oceanic settings (MORB and OIB). Figure 3.2 shows that the composition of a basalt from the Mariana arc has a more 'spiky' pattern than MORB (mid-ocean ridge basalt) and OIB (ocean island basalt). The island arc basalt (IAB) shows enrichment in the highly incompatible elements such as Rb and Ba, depletions in Nb (niobium) and Ta (tantalum), and enrichment in Sr.

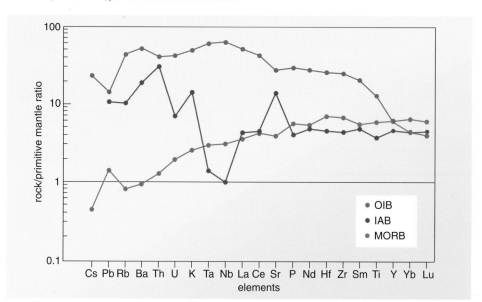

Figure 3.2 Abundances of trace elements in a sample of island arc basalt (IAB) from the oceanic Mariana arc, western Pacific, compared with MORB and an average OIB, and normalized to element concentrations in the primitive mantle.

The distinctive trace element pattern of the arc basalt can be accounted for in terms of two effects. On the one hand, the enrichment (relative to MORB) of the highly incompatible elements (Rb, K, Ba, Sr) can be explained by partial melting of a source that is enriched in these elements but is otherwise similar to that which generates MORB. Because Rb, K, Ba and Sr form ions in aqueous solutions and/or are relatively abundant in the sedimentary layers of subducting slabs, they may be readily transported by fluids that escape from the slab to the mantle during subduction. The depletion of Nb and Ta in arc basalt, on the other hand, may be explained if these elements are held back in the unmelted residue during partial melting, perhaps because a mineral in which these elements are compatible is stabilized in the subduction-modified mantle. While the details of these processes continue to excite the imagination of research geochemists, it is sufficient only to appreciate that the distinctive trace element patterns of arc basalts attest to partial melting of mantle peridotite under conditions that differ from those at mid-ocean ridges and hot spots.

3.3 Causes and conditions of partial melting in the mantle wedge

Because the magmas that erupt at arc volcanoes contain more water, chlorine and other volatiles than MORB or OIB, the mantle source of the arc magmas must be richer in volatiles. Whereas in Block 2 the melting behaviour of dry peridotite was used to understand how MORB and OIB are generated, water-bearing peridotite (or 'wet' peridotite) is appropriate when considering the generation of arc basalts.

BK2. 2.6.

While a tiny amount of water (a few hundred ppm) can be accommodated in the crystal lattices of the nominally anhydrous minerals in 'dry' peridotite, if any more water is present, then hydrous minerals must be present. The identity of these hydrous minerals (and their modal abundance, in other words the proportion in which they are present) depends on the amount of water and also the pressure and temperature of the peridotite. Partial melting reactions then depend on the identity of these phases, so a thorough study of the melting behaviour of 'wet' peridotite would be a detailed one. There is, however, one fairly straightforward result. In Figure 3.3 you can compare the solidus of dry (anhydrous) peridotite (from Block 2) and the solidus of peridotite that coexists with water vapour (based on a compilation of results from five separate studies).

- In what way does the solidus of anhydrous peridotite differ from that of wet peridotite?

- The anhydrous solidus is at a higher temperature than the hydrous solidus, at a given pressure.

As a general rule, the melting temperature of a rock is higher under dry conditions than under wet conditions. In the case of peridotite at mantle pressures ($P \geq 1\,\text{GPa}$), the water lowers the solidus by several hundred degrees Celsius.

If the solidus curves define the minimum temperatures required for melting at particular depths, then the geotherm in the wedge should indicate which parts are likely to be partially molten. The temperatures in the wedge will be controlled by two factors — one of these is the obvious expectation that

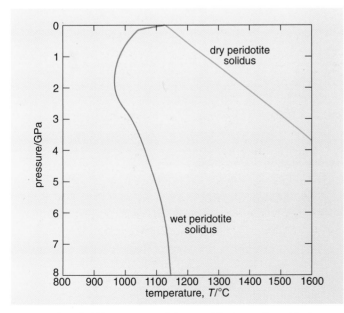

Figure 3.3   Solidus curves of dry peridotite and peridotite with water vapour.

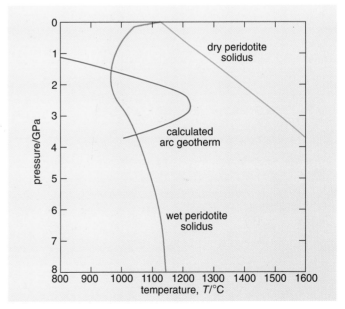

Figure 3.4   The solidi for wet and dry peridotite and a calculated geotherm in the mantle wedge below a volcanic front. The geotherm stops at the top of the slab at a depth of 115 km because, at deeper levels, the solidus of mantle peridotite is no longer relevant.

temperature increases with depth. The second important factor in subduction zones is that a relatively cold slab of oceanic lithosphere is sinking into the hot mantle. So, as Figure 2.12 showed, travelling vertically downwards beneath the volcanic front, temperature will increase before eventually decreasing as the surface of the cold slab is approached. This leads to the hottest part of the mantle wedge being found at some depth between the Moho and the top of the slab. The details of the geotherm will depend on the age of the subducting slab (and therefore how cold it was when subducted) and the angle and speed of subduction (as these factors influence the speed at which heat is moved by mantle material being dragged around the wedge by the action of the sinking slab). One example is shown in Figure 3.4.

●　What do the shapes and positions of the geotherm and solidus curves in Figure 3.4 imply about magma generation conditions in the mantle wedge?

●　Partial melting takes place wherever the geotherm is at a higher temperature than the local solidus. Temperatures in the mantle wedge never exceed the dry solidus, but they do exceed the wet solidus. It follows that for partial melting to take place in the mantle wedge below the volcanic front, at least part of the mantle must be hydrous.

●　What evidence have you already met that suggests the mantle wedge contains water?

●　The high water content and high abundances of volatile–mobile trace elements in arc basalts.

The source of this water must be the subducted slab of oceanic lithosphere, the uppermost parts of which comprise hydrothermally altered MORB, deep-sea sediment and some continent- or island arc-derived sediment. As these materials subduct, increasing pressure and temperature lead to volatiles being driven off in a sequence of metamorphic chemical reactions that produce less hydrous minerals. These are known as **dehydration reactions**. A complex series of dehydration reactions occur as the slab sinks further into the mantle, with the anhydrous silicate minerals also being involved in the metamorphism. One recent estimate, based on experiments at high pressures and temperatures, of how the whole mineral assemblage changes with depth is shown in Figure 3.5.

Figure 3.5c shows that once the oceanic crust has subducted to depths greater than a few tens of kilometres, metamorphism will have combined the iron and magnesium from the original igneous silicate minerals with water to produce a blue, sodium-bearing amphibole and green chlorite. Similarly, the mineral lawsonite (a Ca–Al silicate with about 11% water) accounts for much of the original calcium. At this stage, the rocks have reached what is known as blueschist metamorphic facies (Figure 3.5a).

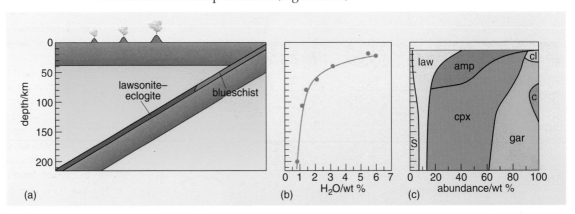

Figure 3.5　(a) Sketch cross-section of a subduction zone alongside a summary of (b) the changing water content and (c) mineralogy of basalt/gabbro oceanic crust as it subducts. S, silica; law, lawsonite; amp, amphibole; cl, chlorite; c, chloritoid; cpx, clinopyroxene; gar, garnet.

◉ At 200 km depth, which minerals are stable?

◉ Silica, lawsonite, clinopyroxene and garnet are stable, with garnet and clinopyroxene making up more than 80% of the rock.

The only hydrous mineral present at 200 km is lawsonite, and the overall water content of the rock is much less than at, say, 20 km (Figure 3.5b). At such very high pressures, virtually all of the rock's atoms are contained in pyroxene and garnet, with the pyroxene being a special variety containing high amounts of Na and Al. Rocks that are composed of roughly equal amounts of pyroxene and garnet are known as **eclogite** (pronounced 'eck-low-jite'). Note that at around 100 km depth, a small amount of chloritoid (Mg–Al silicate with about 8% water) is present. This is not the place to dwell on the chemical compositions of the various minerals; what is of interest, however, is the way in which the water content and mineralogy of the rock change with increasing depth. The next question deals with this.

Question 3.2 According to Figure 3.5, (a) over what depth range does the water content decrease most rapidly, and (b) which minerals are consumed by the dehydration reactions over that depth range?

Thus, dehydration is dominated by breakdown of amphibole and growth of clinopyroxene and garnet, with a blueschist assemblage being replaced by an eclogite assemblage. As well as the chemical changes of metamorphism, there is also an important physical effect due to eclogite having a much higher density than blueschist. The increase in the overall density of the slab directly increases the slab–pull force responsible for driving plate motion at the surface.

The complex series of dehydration reactions results in a long zone over which subducted water is driven off the slab and migrates into the mantle wedge, providing the wet peridotite needed to form arc basalt. If the key process in priming the wedge for magma generation is the addition of water, then the depth at which water is added should be linked to the location of the volcanic front within the subduction zone. Because the depth from the surface to the slab beneath the volcanic front is close to 110 ± 20 km (Figure 2.22b), a popular model for magma generation is that a major dehydration reaction occurs at or near this depth, adding water to the mantle and triggering magma generation (Figure 3.6a) 110 ± 20 km below the volcanoes. Two further observations suggest that things may not always be this simple. First, the metamorphic dehydration reactions in the slab occur over a wide range of depths, and secondly, the seismic tomography of the NE Japan arc (Figure 3.1) indicates magma generation at around 200 km and a sloping rather than vertical path of magma rise. This has led to a modified version of the earlier model. Here (Figure 3.6b), the sinking slab drags the adjacent mantle to deeper levels, setting up the

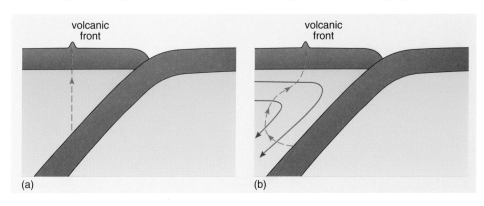

(a) (b)

Figure 3.6 Cross-sections showing (a) a model of magma generation involving slab dehydration and melting directly below the volcanic front, and (b) a model of magma generation involving slab dehydration and flow of mantle in the wedge. Broken lines in (a) and (b) depict the paths taken by the magma and/or partially molten mantle that supplies volcanoes on the volcanic front. The unbroken lines in (b) depict the mantle's flow pattern in the wedge.

pattern of flow in the corner of the wedge that was introduced in Figure 2.12. To account for the seismic tomography data, significant amounts of melting must be inhibited until the hydrated mantle reaches 150 to 200 km depth. Magmas and partially molten mantle then escape the downgoing current and rise through the wedge, being swept towards the trench by the corner flow but escaping into the crust. Although subduction zones vary in the age of the slab and angle of subduction, the combinations of dehydration depths, mantle temperatures and mantle flow pattern somehow conspire to place the volcanic front about 110 km above the slab.

3.4   The source of back-arc magmas

Section 2.5 described the tectonic and volcanic activity that develops behind some volcanic arcs, notably those in the western Pacific. In many respects, back-arc magmatism is similar to that of mid-ocean ridges in that new oceanic crust is generated by stretching and sea-floor spreading. In sea-floor spreading at mid-ocean ridges, magmas are generated by decompression of normal mantle, as described in Block 2, Section 2.4. In subduction zones, however, the mantle wedge is contaminated by elements driven off the subducting slab, and the steady descent of the slab induces a flow of mantle material around the wedge, as shown in Figure 3.6.

- ⬤ Would you expect back-arc basalts to have the compositional affinities of MORB or arc basalts?

- ⬤ Because sea-floor spreading and therefore decompression melting is involved at back-arc spreading, some similarity with MORB might be expected. On the other hand, if the source mantle has been contaminated by subduction zone fluids, the trace element composition of back-arc basalts might be expected to be closer to that of arc basalts.

It is possible to explore this by doing an experiment. To the west of the Tonga arc, in the south-west Pacific, a triangular-shaped ocean basin known as the Lau Basin is the bathymetric expression of back-arc spreading (Figure 3.7). In the south of the Lau Basin, the spreading axis lies closer to the active volcanic arc than it does in the north, so that any influence of subduction zone fluids on back-arc magma composition should diminish northwards. The experiment, then, is to investigate the extent to which the trace element signature of subduction processes is present in back-arc magmas formed at different distances from the arc (or trench). Figure 3.2 has already shown us that, compared to MORB, arc basalts are enriched in elements such as K, Rb and Ba and depleted in Nb and Ta. The ratio of the concentration of one of these enriched elements to the concentration of a depleted element will therefore be much higher in arc basalt than in MORB. For example, the Ba/Nb ratio of the arc basalt and MORB samples plotted in Figure 3.2 are 190 and 2.7 respectively. (*Note:* these values are the ratios of the measured concentrations of Ba and Nb, whereas Figure 3.2 shows concentrations that have been divided by the concentration in primitive mantle.) While these exact values are not shared by every arc or MORB basalt, the large contrast, covering almost two orders of magnitude, means that the Ba/Nb ratio provides a useful relative measure of how arc-like or how MORB-like a particular basalt is. As the very large range of the Ba/Nb ratio is far too great to be accounted for by different degrees of partial melting (see Block 2, Activity 2.3), it must instead reflect a fundamental difference in the composition of the mantle source in these two environments.

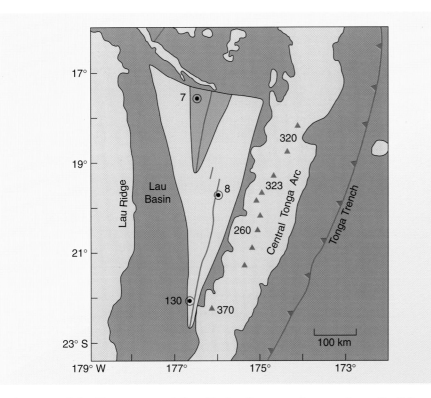

Figure 3.7 Map of the Tonga arc and Lau Basin, in the south-west Pacific. Green denotes new oceanic crust produced by back-arc sea-floor spreading at the ridges identified as red lines. Darker green area denotes oceanic crust formed at the northern spreading ridge, offset from the southerly ridges. Pale blue denotes areas with water depths less than 2 km. Red triangles (other than those showing the Tonga Trench) mark positions of arc volcanoes. Black circles are sampling locations of Lau Basin basalts. Numbers are Ba/Nb ratios of basalt samples.

In the case of the Tonga arc and Lau Basin, the arc volcanoes have Ba/Nb ratios of around 300, which fits with the obvious setting of these volcanoes.

○ Turning to the back-arc basalts, what conclusions can be drawn from the Ba/Nb ratios of the three Lau Basin basalts shown on Figure 3.7?

● These have much lower Ba/Nb ratios than the Tongan lavas, so must come from regions of the mantle that are less affected by subduction. Nonetheless, the back-arc samples have higher ratios than typical MORB. The Ba/Nb ratio decreases as the distance from the eruption site to the arc increases, so the degree of subduction zone influence is less in the north than in the south.

A pictorial representation of the conclusion of this experiment is shown in Figure 3.8, with the region of the mantle influenced by materials emanating from the subducted slab extending to the southern back-arc spreading zone but not to the northern zone.

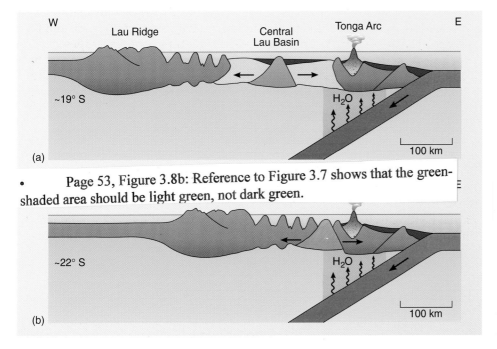

•   Page 53, Figure 3.8b: Reference to Figure 3.7 shows that the green-shaded area should be light green, not dark green.

Figure 3.8 Schematic cross-sections through the Lau Basin–Tonga arc system at (a) 19° S and (b) 22° S.

3.5   Summary of Section 3

- Regions of reduced seismic wave speed in the mantle wedge identify partially molten zones where arc magmas are generated.

- Primitive arc basalts have major element and trace element properties that are inconsistent with an origin by partial melting of subducted basaltic oceanic crust, but are consistent with partial melting of peridotite in the mantle wedge.

- A series of metamorphic dehydration reactions transform subducted altered oceanic crust to anhydrous eclogite, with most water being driven off the slab in the first 100 km of descent.

- Water added to the mantle wedge from the slab lowers the solidus of peridotite, triggering the formation of basalt by partial melting.

- The mantle-normalized trace element pattern of arc basalt shows distinctive enrichments in elements that are readily transported by water-rich fluids (K, Rb, Ba) and strong depletions in Nb and Ta.

- Back-arc basalts have mantle-normalized trace element patterns that are transitional between those of MORB and arc basalts, reflecting generation by decompression melting of mantle that has been influenced by subduction.

Objectives for Section 3

Now that you have completed this Section, you should be able to:

3.1   Understand the meaning of all the terms printed in **bold**.

3.2   Account for the origin of basalts at subduction zones in terms of the compositions of likely source material, their partial melting products and the compositions of the erupted basalts.

3.3   Describe differences between the mantle-normalized trace element pattern of arc basalts and basalts from mid-ocean ridges and hot spots.

3.4   Describe differences between the partial melting behaviour of wet and dry peridotite.

3.5   Describe and briefly explain the main metamorphic dehydration reactions within oceanic crust as it subducts to depths of about 200 km.

3.6   Describe trace element evidence for the origin of back-arc basalts.

4   Evolution of magmas at subduction zones

You have already found that the lavas and pyroclastic material erupted from arc volcanoes are rarely primary magmas — their compositions are more differentiated, with higher SiO_2 and lower Mg-numbers. In this Section, you will learn some more about the compositional variation of subduction zone magmas, the processes that produce this variation, and their implications for the evolution of Earth's crust. If the magmas leaving the mantle wedge are primitive basalts, but evolved magmas in the range basaltic andesite to rhyolite erupt at the surface, then it must be during their passage through the crust that the chemical composition of the magmas changes. Given the existence of eruptions that disgorge several cubic kilometres or more of magma and which lead to caldera collapse, it is likely that sub-volcanic magma chambers of at least this volume are the main sites of magma storage and compositional evolution.

- Magmas can evolve in chemical composition by the removal of material and by the addition of material. In what ways can these subtractions and additions be achieved?

- Crystals growing in the magma can be removed, leaving an evolved magma that is poor in the elements contained in the crystals and enriched in elements that are excluded by the crystals. The magma composition can also change if the hot magma digests crustal rocks of a different composition.

Distinguishing between the different processes by which magmas evolve can be done by investigating the chemical variation of the igneous rocks at a single volcanic centre, as this reflects the chemical composition of the subtracted or added materials. The volcanic rocks from Santorini, particularly the lavas from the Skaros shield volcano (Figures 2.23b and 2.24b), will serve as an example with which to work, but first we need to define some rock names on the basis of chemical composition.

4.1   Chemical compositions of arc magmas

Igneous rocks cover a very broad range of chemical composition, so some subdivision into a systematic framework is helpful and this is usually achieved using one or more chemical plots such as the total alkalis against silica plot introduced earlier. Over the years, geochemists have found that several such plots are useful, but while no single one is regarded as a universal 'industry standard', a few are in such common usage that they underpin geologists' vocabulary. The key diagrams are introduced here.

4.1.1   The K_2O against SiO_2 plot

A diagram that is commonly used to display the compositions of volcanic rocks from subduction zones is the graph of K_2O against SiO_2 given in Figure 4.1. The vertical lines divide the rocks into basalt, basaltic–andesite, andesite, dacite and rhyolite according to their SiO_2 content. Occasionally, the term rhyodacite is used for rocks with 68 to 72% SiO_2. Incidentally, the SiO_2 contents defining the boundaries between basalt and basaltic andesite and between basaltic andesite and andesite are different on Figures 2.25 (total alkalis vs. SiO_2) and 4.1 (K_2O vs. SiO_2), highlighting the arbitrariness of the divisions.

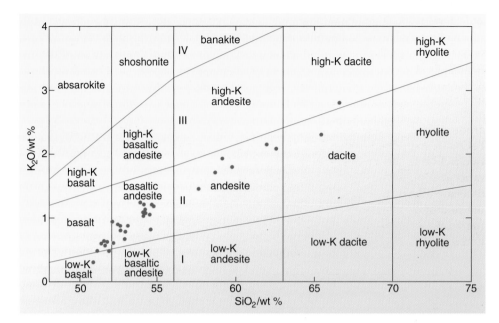

Figure 4.1 Plot of K$_2$O (wt %) against SiO$_2$ (wt %) showing the nomenclature of volcanic rocks. Red lines divide the graph into the groups labelled I–IV. Plotted points are analyses of lavas from the Skaros shield, Santorini.

The sloping (red) lines separate the four groups I to IV. Of these groups, I, II and III are known as the **low-K**, **medium-K** and **high-K series** respectively, while group IV, an unusually potassic group of rare magmas, are the **shoshonite series**. Magmas from a given volcano typically fall into one of the low-, medium- or high-K series. Figure 4.1 is therefore not solely a way of classifying a single rock, but also a way of classifying an entire series of rock samples from a volcano.

Question 4.1 (a) To which series do most of the Skaros lavas belong? (b) Table 4.1 lists analyses of six lavas from the Skaros shield. On the basis of their SiO$_2$ contents, assign each rock a name and complete the 'rock type' row in Table 4.1.

Table 4.1 Chemical composition of selected rocks from the Skaros shield. Major element oxides in wt %; trace elements in parts per million (ppm). See Box 4.1 for an explanation of FeO$_t$.

Sample	181	180	182	178	171	153
Rock type						
SiO$_2$	50.81	51.83	52.84	54.47	62.50	66.44
TiO$_2$	0.75	0.77	0.82	0.90	0.82	0.67
Al$_2$O$_3$	18.74	18.26	18.01	18.49	16.10	15.37
FeO$_t$	8.28	7.94	8.22	7.84	5.54	4.66
MnO	0.17	0.16	0.18	0.17	0.14	0.15
MgO	6.44	6.21	5.89	4.35	1.74	1.07
CaO	11.37	11.29	10.77	9.61	4.71	2.58
Na$_2$O	2.25	2.44	2.57	3.03	4.49	5.16
K$_2$O	0.31	0.48	0.66	1.04	2.07	2.79
P$_2$O$_5$	0.08	0.09	0.10	0.12	0.22	0.20
total	99.20	99.47	100.06	100.02	98.33	99.09
Rb	9	17	22	38	69	93
Sr	221	207	212	221	188	136
Th	1.1	2.7	3.4	6.4	12.4	16.0
Ni	34	35	31	12	6	1
V	285	264	265	246	85	–
Sc	37	39	37	32	19	11
Zr	65	80	93	124	234	290

4.1.2 The FeO_t/MgO against SiO_2 plot

A second means of classifying igneous rock series relies on the observation that some sub-alkaline igneous rocks have higher ratios of iron to magnesium, at a given SiO_2 content, than other igneous rocks. This difference has been exploited to distinguish two rock series on the basis of the ratio of the total amount of iron oxide FeO_t to MgO (Figure 4.2). (As an aside, the reasons behind using the amount of total iron oxide, FeO_t, sometimes to be found written as FeO_{total} or $FeO*$, are explained in Box 4.1.) The FeO_t/MgO versus SiO_2 diagram is split into two fields, as shown in Figure 4.2. Rocks with comparatively high FeO_t/MgO ratios belong to the **tholeiitic series**, whereas low FeO_t/MgO ratios are a feature of a **calc-alkaline series**. (The term calc-alkaline is inherited from an older method of classification based on the silica content within a rock series at which the wt % CaO = wt % Na_2O + K_2O, but the details of this do not concern us here.)

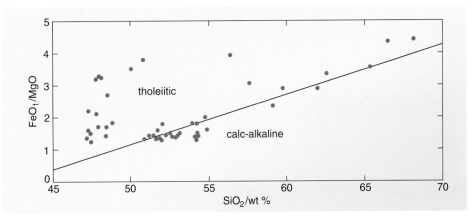

Figure 4.2 Plot of FeO_t/MgO against SiO_2 showing the fields of tholeiitic and calc-alkaline rocks. The plotted analyses are from Iceland (purple) and Santorini (red).

Box 4.1 Notes on FeO, Fe_2O_3 and FeO_t

In nature, iron can occur as Fe^{2+} ions and as Fe^{3+} ions. The chemical compositions of rocks, which are normally expressed in terms of oxide components, therefore express the amount of Fe^{2+} as FeO and the amount of Fe^{3+} as Fe_2O_3. In igneous rocks, most of the iron is present as Fe^{2+}, unless the rock has suffered extreme weathering or chemical alteration, in which case Fe^{2+} is oxidized to Fe^{3+} and the Fe^{2+}/Fe^{3+} ratio will be lower than in the original magma. In cases where geochemists use rock analyses to infer the processes responsible for the compositions of magmas, it is therefore more meaningful to consider the total iron content rather than the proportions of FeO and Fe_2O_3, which may have more to do with the vagaries of post-magmatic alteration than with igneous processes.

Nowadays, it is rare for rocks to be analysed by the laborious wet chemical methods by which FeO and Fe_2O_3 contents are determined separately. Instead, rocks are usually analysed by the instrumental technique of X-ray fluorescence spectrometry (XRF) and this provides analyses in which all the iron is reported as Fe_2O_3. In contrast, mineral analyses are routinely undertaken on another instrument, the electron microprobe (Section 4.2.2), and this gives total iron as FeO. As already mentioned, most of the iron in magmas is present as Fe^{2+}, so it is common practice for the total iron content of igneous rocks to be expressed in terms of FeO (denoted as FeO_t), even though the original analytical technique yields a measurement expressed as Fe_2O_3. Given a particular amount of Fe, then the atomic masses of Fe (55.8) and O (16) can be used to show that the wt % FeO is equivalent to 0.9 times the wt % Fe_2O_3. In other words, it is possible to convert from Fe_2O_3 to FeO using FeO = 0.9 Fe_2O_3.

The Skaros samples straddle the dividing line in Figure 4.2, but this is nothing to worry about. The diagram is still useful because (a) it demonstrates, as did Figures 2.25 and 4.1, that the compositions of the rocks at this volcano define a clear series or trend, and (b) it shows how the Santorini rocks have certain differences when compared with other volcanoes. For example, a series of Icelandic lavas (purple dots in Figure 4.2) fall on a trend with higher FeO_t/MgO at a given SiO_2 (within the tholeiitic field) and a different shape from that defined by the Santorini data. The compositional difference between the volcanic rock series from these different plate tectonic settings is obvious.

4.1.3 The AFM diagram

The **AFM diagram** (Figure 4.3) is named after the three components that are plotted:

$$A = Na_2O + K_2O \text{ (the alkalis)}; F = FeO_t; M = MgO.$$

On an AFM diagram, basalts plot close to the FM side of the triangle, far from the A apex, because these magmas are poor in alkalis compared with FeO_t and MgO. Silicic magmas, being rich in alkalis and poor in FeO_t and especially MgO, plot close to the AF side. Progressing from basalt through andesite to dacite, the Santorini and Icelandic analyses each define trends that sweep from right to left across the diagram. These trends ultimately point towards the A apex, as this is where very highly evolved silicic magmas, with low concentrations of iron and magnesium, would plot.

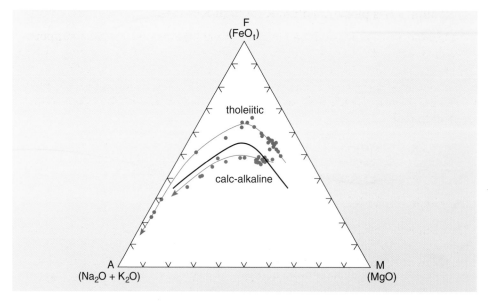

Figure 4.3 AFM diagram showing the fields of tholeiitic and calc-alkaline rocks (separated by the black line). The plotted analyses are from Iceland (purple) and Santorini (red), and they can be described by the drawn trend lines, with the arrows pointing towards more evolved compositions.

The AFM diagram (Figure 4.3) usefully displays a number of important points concerning tholeiitic and calc-alkaline magma compositions. Intermediate members of tholeiitic magma series have high FeO_t/MgO ratios, as was seen in Figure 4.2, and so plot closer to the F apex than do intermediate calc-alkaline magmas. The AFM diagram is thus divided into two regions (Figure 4.3); the upper region contains tholeiitic compositions, the lower region contains calc-alkaline compositions. The boundary between the two fields is somewhat arbitrary and serves exactly the same purpose as the tholeiitic/calc-alkaline boundary in Figure 4.2. On both diagrams, the Icelandic rocks are defined as tholeiitic, whereas those of Santorini are predominantly calc-alkaline. As with the Santorini rocks here, volcanic rocks that plot in the calc-alkaline fields in Figures 4.2 and 4.3 usually plot in the medium-K field in Figure 4.1.

Question 4.2 Confirm that sample 178 in Table 4.1 plots in the calc-alkaline field in Figure 4.3.

On the basis of their chemical composition, Santorini's magmas are basalts, basaltic-andesites, andesites, dacites and rhyolites. Together, they constitute a rock series that can be described using the terms medium-K and calc-alkaline.

Activity 4.1 Comparing the compositions of magmas from different arcs

Now attempt Activity 4.1 in *Workbook 3*, which should take you about 45 minutes. Section 2 showed that, from a geological point of view, subduction zones cover a wide range of types. The volcanic arc may be built on oceanic crust, young continental crust or ancient continental crust. Does this have an effect on the composition of the magmas erupted? Answer this question by comparing the compositions of magmas from different arcs.

4.1.4 Summary of Section 4.1

- Volcanic rocks from arc volcanoes can be classified according to their chemical composition. Individual rocks may be classified according to silica content (basalt, basaltic andesite, etc.). Whole rock series, as defined by coherent trends on chemical variation diagrams, can be classified using diagrams such as K_2O versus SiO_2, FeO_t/MgO versus SiO_2, and the AFM diagram.

- In general, tholeiitic arc series plot in the field of low-K series whereas calc-alkaline series plot as medium-K (or high-K) series.

- Oceanic, thin continental and thick continental arc crust typically support compositionally different arc magma compositions. With increasing thickness and continental character, magma series become more dominated by andesites and dacites at the expense of basalts and basaltic andesites, and the magma series change from tholeiitic or low-K to calc-alkaline or medium- and high-K.

4.2 Magma evolution by fractional crystallization

The chemical compositions of the Skaros lavas on Santorini show good correlations between certain elements (Figures 4.1–4.3) so you would be right to think that this is the result of some systematic process, rather than a random process, determining the magmas' compositions. **Fractional crystallization** is one such process, and operates as follows. As a magma cools and crystallizes, elements that are preferentially incorporated into the growing crystals become impoverished in the remaining liquid. Similarly, elements that are not incorporated into the crystals become enriched in the remaining liquid. If the crystals become separated from the liquid, then a new magma with a different composition will be produced. This is fractional crystallization. By this process, basaltic magmas can potentially give rise to basaltic andesites, which in turn can produce andesite and still more felsic, fractionated (or evolved) magmas such as dacite.

In this Section, you will investigate whether there is evidence for fractional crystallization having generated the basalt–andesite–dacite association found at Santorini. Before starting on this, it is necessary to find out exactly which minerals are present in the Santorini lavas. You will have met most of these minerals in Block 2 or previous Courses but, for reference, they are listed along with their chemical compositions in Box 4.2.

Box 4.2 The minerals typically found in igneous rocks from subduction zones

Mineral name	General chemical composition	Comments
quartz	SiO_2	
plagioclase feldspar	$(CaAl,NaSi,KSi)AlSi_2O_8$	Forms a solid solution series between anorthite ($CaAl_2Si_2O_8$) and albite ($NaAlSi_3O_8$), with a small proportion of orthoclase ($KAlSi_3O_8$).
alkali feldspar	$(Na,K)AlSi_3O_8$	Forms a partial solid solution series between orthoclase and albite, with a small amount of anorthite.
olivine	$(Mg,Fe)_2SiO_4$	Solid solution series between forsterite (Fo: Mg_2SiO_4) and fayalite (Fa: Fe_2SiO_4).
orthopyroxene	$(Mg,Fe,Ca)_2Si_2O_6$	Solid solution series between enstatite (En: $Mg_2Si_2O_6$) and ferrosilite (Fs: $Fe_2Si_2O_6$) with less than 5% wollastonite (Wo: $Ca_2Si_2O_6$).
clinopyroxene	$(Mg,Fe,Ca)_2Si_2O_6$	Clinopyroxenes are distinguished from orthopyroxene in thin section by having inclined, rather than straight, extinction. The variety known as augite is common in basalts and intermediate igneous rocks. It has 20 to 40% Wo.
hornblende	$Ca_2(Mg,Fe)_5Si_8O_{22}(OH)_2$	A member of the mineral group amphibole.
biotite	$K(Mg,Fe)_3AlSi_3O_{10}(OH)_2$	A dark brown variety of mica. The pale variety muscovite has much less Mg and Fe ($KAl_3Si_3O_{10}(OH)_2$).
magnetite	Fe_3O_4	A considerable amount of Ti can enter the magnetite structure at the expense of Fe^{3+}, leading to solid solution with Fe_2TiO_4. Ti-rich magnetite is known as titanomagnetite.
ilmenite	$FeTiO_3$	
apatite	$Ca_5P_3O_{12}(OH,F,Cl)$	
zircon	$ZrSiO_4$	

4.2.1 Mineralogy of Santorini lavas

The Skaros lavas contain between 10 and 35% phenocrysts in a fine-grained or glassy matrix. A thin section of a basalt from Santorini (Figure 4.4a) reveals abundant plagioclase feldspar phenocrysts together with olivine and clinopyroxene. Olivine is less abundant or absent in andesite and dacite (Figure 4.46b and c), with these more-evolved rocks also containing orthopyroxene and magnetite (Figure 4.4c). This information can be summarized in a diagram, such as Figure 4.5, showing whether given minerals are present or absent in rocks of a particular SiO_2 content. Where the bar fades, the mineral in question is only sometimes present in that SiO_2 range.

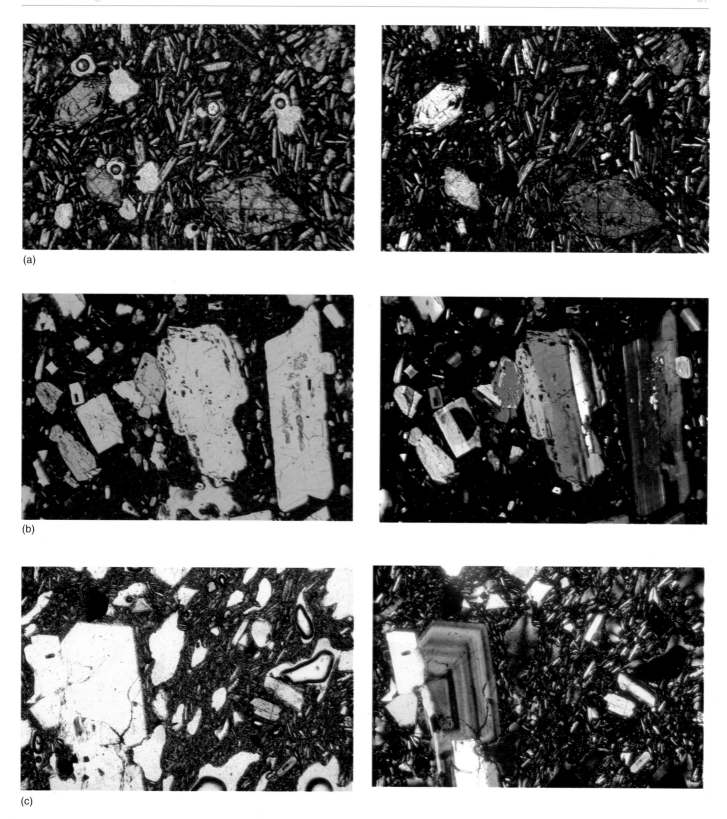

Figure 4.4 Photomicrographs of (a) basalt, (b) andesite and (c) dacite from Santorini. Photomicrographs are in plane-polarized light (left-hand column) and crossed polars (right-hand column). Field of view is 1 mm wide.

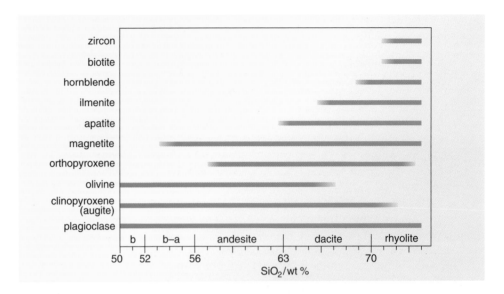

Figure 4.5 Diagrammatic summary of the correlation between modal mineralogy and rock compositions in volcanic rocks from Santorini. Rock names are based on the classification in Figure 4.1; b = basalt, b–a = basaltic andesite.

Where they occur, the minerals titanomagnetite (Fe_2TiO_4), ilmenite ($FeTiO_3$), apatite ($Ca_5P_3O_{12}(OH,F,Cl)$) and zircon ($ZrSiO_4$) are present in small amounts (usually <1% of the rock) and are referred to as accessory minerals.

● What correlations are there between the modal mineralogy of the rocks and their chemical composition?

● The low-silica rocks contain a phenocryst assemblage of olivine + clinopyroxene + plagioclase. At higher silica content, orthopyroxene appears and olivine disappears from the phenocryst assemblage. Titanomagnetite is present in some basaltic andesites and all more evolved rock compositions. The other accessory minerals (apatite, ilmenite and zircon) appear at higher SiO_2 contents and phenocrysts of the hydrous minerals hornblende and biotite sometimes occur in the most evolved magmas.

Sometimes, the compositionally defined boundaries between rock names roughly coincide with mineralogical changes, which is one reason why the compositional boundaries have been drawn in particular places. The link between chemical composition and mineralogy suggests that the chemical composition of the magma controls which minerals will grow (i.e., what types of phenocrysts will be present).

4.2.2 Mineral compositions

Apart from zircon and apatite, all of the main phenocryst phases in the Skaros rocks belong to mineral groups that are **solid solution series**. When you considered the phase diagram of the olivine binary solid solution series forsterite (Fo) – fayalite (Fa), you found that a Fo-rich liquid would precipitate an olivine that was more Fo-rich than olivine precipitated from a Fo-poor liquid. This was the basis for using Mg-number to identify liquids that were in equilibrium with Fo-rich mantle olivine in Block 2 (Section 2.5.1). This idea extends to other minerals — an MgO-rich magma will precipitate phenocrysts of MgO-rich olivine and pyroxene. Similarly, a CaO-rich magma will precipitate anorthite-rich plagioclase phenocrysts. If the magma and its minerals are in chemical equilibrium, then there should be a close correlation between mineral and rock compositions. To test whether this is the case, geologists take advantage of analytical instruments that allow individual crystals in rocks to be analysed down to a spatial resolution of several micrometres (see Box 4.3 Mineral analysis techniques). The results allow you to discover if the compositions of olivine, clinopyroxene, orthopyroxene and plagioclase in the Santorini lavas are related to the composition of the rocks in which they are found.

Box 4.3 Mineral analysis techniques

The precise composition of a mineral can be found by separating it from a crushed rock sample and making a chemical analysis. However, other minerals may be accidentally included in the analysed material, being either present as inclusions within the crystal of interest or as loose crystals that failed to be separated out during sample preparation. To overcome these difficulties, a different method is required. This relies on an instrument known as the **electron microprobe**. In this technique, a thin section of rock with a highly polished surface is specially prepared and placed in a vacuum chamber. A focused beam of electrons is then directed onto an area a few micrometres across on the sample's surface. The electron beam causes this tiny region to emit X-rays of a character dependent on the chemical composition of the bombarded material. These X-rays are monitored by a detector, enabling the composition of the targeted spot to be obtained. Several analyses can be made across a single crystal, building a detailed picture of any compositional zoning. This would be impossible to detect, let alone measure, by just analysing a composite sample of grains separated from the rock; such a method would only give the average composition. Using the microprobe, different crystals of the same mineral within a single thin section can be analysed to check for variation. This type of detail is invaluable in answering many petrological questions, including some aspects of Santorini's magmatism.

Olivine compositions are reported in terms of the proportions of forsterite (Fo: Mg_2SiO_4) and fayalite (Fa: Fe_2SiO_4). The forsterite content of the cores of olivine phenocrysts decreases with decreasing MgO in the whole rock (Figure 4.6).

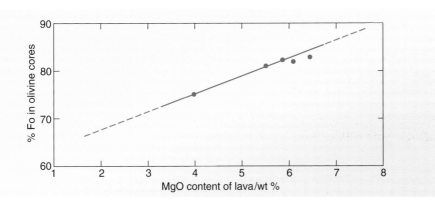

Figure 4.6 Correlation between the forsterite (Fo) content of olivine and the MgO content of their host lava. Data are from Skaros, and the broken lines extrapolate the trend to compositions found elsewhere.

Pyroxene contains the Ca, Mg and Fe end-members wollastonite (Wo: $Ca_2Si_2O_6$), enstatite (En: $Mg_2Si_2O_6$) and ferrosilite (Fs: $Fe_2Si_2O_6$). Pyroxene rarely contains more than 50% of the Wo component, and then only slightly more than 50%. Such extreme compositions are found in some alkali-rich igneous rocks. More normally, pyroxenes have compositions which lie in what is known as the **pyroxene quadrilateral** shown in Figure 4.7. This diagram is the lower half of a triangular diagram with En, Fs and Wo at its corners. The corners of the quadrilateral are defined by the compositions En, Fs, diopside (Di: $CaMgSi_2O_6$, i.e. $En_{50}Fs_0Wo_{50}$) and hedenbergite (Hd: $CaFeSi_2O_6$, i.e. $En_0Fs_{50}Wo_{50}$). The variety of clinopyroxene known as **augite** contains substantial quantities of calcium and so plots in the upper part of the quadrilateral, in the direction of the Wo corner. Orthopyroxene contains only minor amounts of calcium and so plots close to the enstatite (En) – ferrosilite (Fs) join.

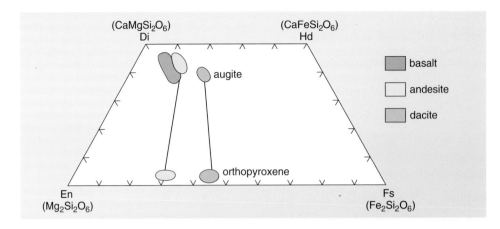

Figure 4.7 The pyroxene quadrilateral, showing the compositions of augite in basalt, andesite and dacite, and of orthopyroxene in andesite and dacite. Lines join co-existing augite and orthopyroxene compositions.

Basalt contains the most magnesian augites, and they plot near the diopside (Di) corner of the quadrilateral (Figure 4.7). Andesites and dacites contain less MgO than basalt (Table 4.1), so that pyroxenes that crystallize from these magmas are more Fe-rich and so plot further to the right in the pyroxene quadrilateral. Both augite and orthopyroxene are present in these more evolved magmas, and in Figure 4.7, lines join the co-existing compositions, illustrating the shift to less magnesian mineral compositions with decreasing MgO in the rock.

To relate a pyroxene crystal's composition to its position to the left (Mg-rich) or right (Fe-rich) of Figure 4.7, it is convenient to quote its Mg-number defined as

$$\text{Mg-number} = 100 \times \text{Mg}/(\text{Mg} + \text{Fe}) \qquad (4.1)$$

or, equivalently,

$$\text{Mg-number} = 100 \times \text{En}/(\text{En} + \text{Fs}) \qquad (4.2)$$

because En and Fs are the pure Mg and Fe end-members.

> **Question 4.3** (a) One of the basalts from Skaros contains augite of composition $\text{En}_{47.1}\text{Fs}_{12.4}\text{Wo}_{40.5}$. What is the Mg-number of this crystal?
> (b) Using Figure 4.7, estimate the composition of augite in Skaros dacite and determine its Mg-number.

Will the Mg-number of pyroxenes increase or decrease with MgO content of the host rock? Augite compositions from several Skaros lavas are plotted against the host rocks' MgO content in Figure 4.8. The correlation that emerges from Figure 4.8 is similar to that found with the olivines. A magma with a low MgO content will precipitate ferromagnesian minerals that are poor in magnesium.

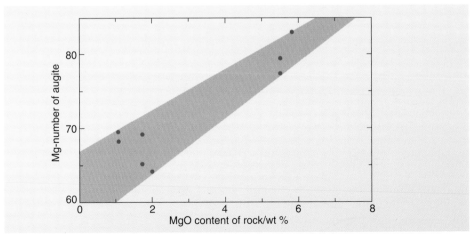

Figure 4.8 Plot showing the Mg-number of augite in Skaros lavas and the MgO content of the host rock.

Plagioclase composition also depends on the composition of the bulk rock. This relationship is summarized in Table 4.2. So, in parallel with a decrease in the Mg-number of ferromagnesian minerals, the anorthite content of plagioclase phenocrysts decreases in more evolved magmas.

Table 4.2 Correlation between the composition of plagioclase and its host rock among Skaros lavas.

Rock type	Wt % SiO_2 in rock	Wt % CaO in rock	Anorthite content of plagioclase
basalt	< 52	> 10.5	94–75
basaltic andesite	52–56	8–10.5	89–71
andesite	56–63	4–8	80–50
dacite	> 63	< 4	65–40

The systematic correlations between mineral composition and rock composition that you have found in this Section can be explained if the phenocrysts grew from liquids with the composition of the whole rocks. This simple and perhaps expected relationship suggests that crystallization of these magmas obeys simple rules that determine mineral composition.

4.2.3 Investigating fractional crystallization using major elements

Given the composition of the phenocrysts growing in basalt, can we determine whether it is feasible to derive an andesite with 57% SiO_2 by the removal of plagioclase, augite and olivine from a basalt with 51% SiO_2? If this is the process by which andesites evolve from basalt, then the compositional path from basalt to andesite has to lead away from the composition of a mixture of the three proposed minerals. One way of testing whether this is the case is to plot a variation diagram showing the compositions of the rocks and minerals proposed to be related by fractional crystallization. Figure 4.9 and Question 4.4 give you the chance to do this.

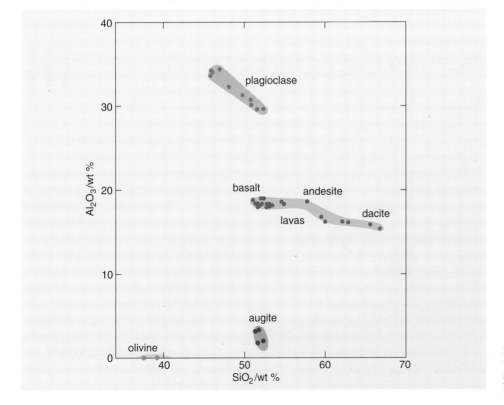

Figure 4.9 Variation diagram of Al_2O_3 versus SiO_2. The red points are lavas from Skaros, and the grey and green data points are minerals in basalt lava.

Question 4.4 With reference to Figure 4.9, answer the following. (a) What is the approximate Al_2O_3 content of a plagioclase + augite + olivine mineral extract that would be required to generate the andesite from the basalt? (b) Estimate, to the nearest 10%, the proportion of plagioclase in the mineral extract. (c) How might the kink in the Al_2O_3 versus SiO_2 trend at $SiO_2 \approx 57\%$ have originated?

For an igneous rock series produced by fractional crystallization, sudden changes in the slope of trends on variation diagrams should coincide with the appearance or disappearance of minerals from the assemblage of minerals crystallizing.

Question 4.5 (a) Given the chemical compositions of olivine, augite, plagioclase, orthopyroxene, titanomagnetite and apatite (see Box 4.2), how would you expect the concentrations of TiO_2, FeO_t and P_2O_5 to change due to fractional crystallization? (b) Figure 4.10 shows plots of TiO_2, FeO_t and P_2O_5 against SiO_2 with the overall variation trends shown by lines. Are the trends on these variation diagrams consistent with fractional crystallization being a dominant control on magma evolution? (*Hint:* recall that Figure 4.5 shows how the mineral assemblage changes with increasing SiO_2 content.)

The good correlation between the sense of element enrichment or depletion with increasing SiO_2 and the concentrations of those elements in the observed phenocryst assemblages is strong evidence in support of fractional crystallization.

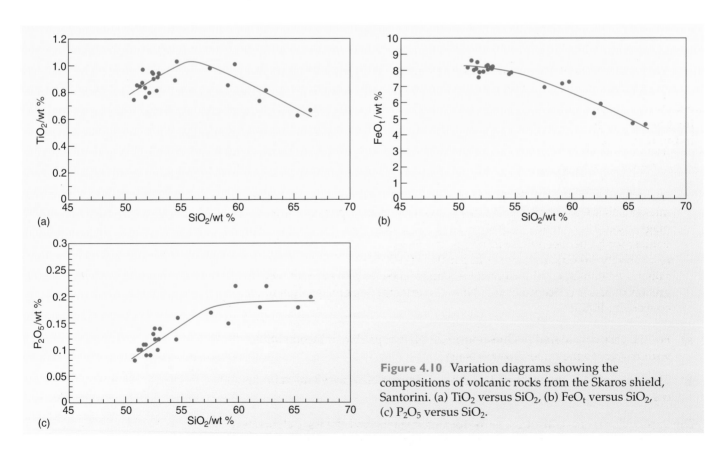

(a)

(b)

(c)

Figure 4.10 Variation diagrams showing the compositions of volcanic rocks from the Skaros shield, Santorini. (a) TiO_2 versus SiO_2, (b) FeO_t versus SiO_2, (c) P_2O_5 versus SiO_2.

4.2.4 Investigating fractional crystallization using trace elements

Trace elements are useful in studies of igneous processes, and in Block 2 for example you used trace element patterns to compare basalts from different settings. As well as using the shape of the trace element patterns to simply describe or classify the different basalts, it was possible to link the patterns to different conditions of partial melting in the mantle and to different compositions of the mantle sources. This Section extends your experience of using trace elements by considering how variation in trace element concentrations in lavas from a volcano can be used to recognize the processes operating within a magma chamber.

Trace elements provide a useful tool for investigating partial melting and fractional crystallization. This is because these processes rely on there being chemical equilibrium between crystals and liquid and, as you found in Block 2, the concentration of a given trace element in an igneous mineral is proportional to its concentration in the silicate liquid in chemical equilibrium with the crystal. It follows that trace elements should behave in particular predictable ways, depending on whether partial melting or fractional crystallization is occurring. As a result, trace element variation in a suite of lavas can indicate which processes operated.

The lynchpins are the **mineral partition coefficient, K_d,** and the **bulk partition coefficient, D,** that were defined in Block 2 — for a given element and a given mineral:

$$K_d = \frac{\text{concentration in the mineral}}{\text{concentration in the liquid}} \tag{4.3}$$

$$D = \frac{\text{concentration in the mineral assemblage}}{\text{concentration in the liquid}} \tag{4.4}$$

For a mineral assemblage containing three minerals A, B and C, in mass fractions x_A, x_B and x_C, then the bulk partition coefficient is related to the individual mineral partition coefficients by the equation:

$$D = x_A K_{dA} + x_B K_{dB} + x_C K_{dC} \tag{4.5}$$

> **Question 4.6** Consider the trace element nickel (Ni) and an assemblage of minerals that have crystallized from a magma in the proportions 60% plagioclase, 10% augite and 30% olivine. The partition coefficients (K_d values) for Ni between these minerals and liquid are 0.01, 2.0 and 6.2 respectively. (a) Calculate the bulk partition coefficient (D) for Ni for this mineral assemblage. (b) According to your answer to part (a), will there be a greater or lesser concentration of Ni in the mineral assemblage than in the co-existing liquid?

- For the case considered in Question 4.6, is Ni compatible or incompatible with respect to the mineral assemblage?

- The value of D is greater than 1, so Ni is a compatible trace element in this case.

During fractional crystallization, early-formed crystals (and the trace elements they contain) are continuously removed from chemical contact with the residual liquid. The amount of a trace element in the liquid therefore changes in concentration from the original amount, C_0, to some new concentration, C_1.

● What variables do you think will influence the size of the difference between C_0 and C_1 during fractional crystallization of a magma?

● The two variables of importance are the bulk partition coefficient D, which determines how strongly a given element is removed from the liquid into the phenocrysts, and the amount of crystallization.

The amount of crystallization is gauged by considering the mass fraction of the initial liquid that remains:

$$F = \frac{\text{mass of liquid remaining (with composition } C_1)}{\text{mass of liquid at the start (with composition } C_0)} \tag{4.6}$$

● With increasing fractional crystallization, does F increase or decrease?

● F starts at a value of 1 and becomes smaller with increasing degree of crystallization. When the magma is completely crystallized, $F = 0$.

If the bulk partition coefficient for a particular trace element is larger than 1, then the concentration of that element in the liquid will fall rapidly with increasing amounts of fractional crystallization (i.e., decreasing F). And if the bulk partition coefficient has a value of zero, then none of the trace element will enter the crystals and its concentration in the remaining liquid will increase. This behaviour was first set out mathematically by the renowned Victorian physicist Lord Rayleigh in a study addressing a totally different problem (that of separation of a gas from a liquid) and published in 1896. His equation is

$$C_1 = C_0 F^{(D-1)} \tag{4.7}$$

and is one of the most widely used equations in igneous petrology. Equation 4.7 now bears his name, and it is known as the **Rayleigh fractionation equation**.

This equation is useful because it allows us to see how trace element concentrations are expected to change during fractional crystallization, and therefore test whether chemical analyses of suites of volcanic rocks conform with those expected from fractional crystallization.

First of all, let us consider how the enrichment or depletion of a trace element varies with the amount of crystallization. Values of C_1/C_0 are calculated from the equation:

$$C_1/C_0 = F^{(D-1)} \tag{4.8}$$

which is just Equation 4.7 after dividing both sides by C_0. So, we have

for $D = 3$, $C_1/C_0 = F^2$

for $D = 2$, $C_1/C_0 = F^1 = F$

for $D = 1$, $C_1/C_0 = F^0 = 1$

for $D = 0.5$, $C_1/C_0 = F^{-0.5} = F^{-1/2} = 1/\sqrt{F}$

for $D = 0$, $C_1/C_0 = F^{-1} = 1/F$.

Table 4.3 lists C_1/C_0 as a function of F and D, for $D = 3, 2, 1, 0.5$ and 0. We have left you to work out the values that should go in the blank spaces in this Table.

Question 4.7 Complete the listing of C_1/C_0 values in Table 4.3.

Table 4.3 Normalized liquid composition C_l/C_0 as a function of the fraction of liquid remaining, F, during Rayleigh fractionation with bulk partition coefficient D.

F	$D = 3$	$D = 2$	$D = 1$	$D = 0.5$	$D = 0$
1	1.00	1.00	1.00	1.00	1.00
0.9	0.81	0.90	1.00	1.05	1.11
0.8	0.64	0.80	1.00	1.12	1.25
0.7	0.49	0.7	1.0	1.20	1.43
0.6	0.36	0.60	1.00	1.29	1.67
0.5	0.25	0.50	1.00	1.41	2.00
0.4	0.16	0.40	1.00	1.58	2.5
0.3	0.09	0.30	1.00	1.83	3.3
0.2	0.04	0.20	1.00	2.24	5
0.1	0.01	0.10	1.00	3.16	10

It is easier to discuss the results from Question 4.7 after plotting them onto a graph.

Question 4.8 Plot the data from your completed Table 4.3 onto Figure 4.11 so as to derive curves of C_l/C_0 as a function of F for each value of D. (*Hint:* work systematically by plotting all the data for one D value, then draw a smooth curve through the set of data points before plotting the values for the next D curve.)

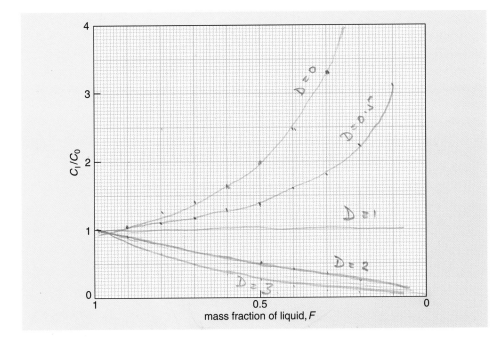

Figure 4.11 Graphical representation of the Rayleigh fractionation equation (for use with Question 4.8).

The results in Figure A4.1 show what was deduced qualitatively a little earlier — compatible elements become depleted most rapidly the larger the value of D. Incompatible trace elements increase in concentration with differentiation. However, D can never have a value less than 0, so in this model of fractional crystallization, the concentration of any trace element can never plot above the curve for $D = 0$ on Figure 4.11. You can use Figure A4.1 (on p.146) to answer the following question.

> **Question 4.9** (a) Consider a parental basalt containing 5 ppm Rb (rubidium). Fractional crystallization of olivine, plagioclase and augite produces andesite magma with 16 ppm Rb. If the bulk partition coefficient for Rb is $D_{Rb} = 0$, what proportion of the original basalt does the fractionated magma represent (i.e., what is the value of F)? (b) The same basalt contains 100 ppm Ni (nickel) and has $D_{Ni} = 2.0$; the andesite has 31 ppm Ni. Does this fit in with your result from part (a)?

To test all the members of an entire rock series for evidence of fractional crystallization using the method of Question 4.9 would be very tedious, especially if we had to deal with many trace elements. Even with a computer to do the calculations, there would still be the problem of deciding what was the composition of the parental magma (i.e., the C_0 values for each trace element). We need a way to overcome these hurdles; could the variation between two trace elements in a rock series be of help here? For any value of F on Figure 4.11 (or Figure A4.1), the ratio C_1/C_0 depends on the value of D. If we take two trace elements with different D values and plot a graph to show the covariation of C_1/C_0 of the two elements, then we arrive at Figure 4.12. This result shows smooth variation of composition depending on the D values of the two elements.

Although Figure 4.12 still involves knowing the composition of the parental magma, it is enticing because it looks as if the shape of a plot of one element against another must follow a particular curved trend if fractional crystallization is responsible. This fractional crystallization trend can be defined by combining the Rayleigh fractionation equations for two elements, 1 and 2, to derive the general equation:

$$C_1 = aC_2{}^m \tag{4.9}$$

where a and m are constants with values that depend on the parental magma composition (C_{01} and C_{02}) and the elements' bulk partition coefficients (D_1 and D_2). This equation provides the rule that defines how two trace elements must co-vary during fractional crystallization under conditions where both bulk partition coefficients do not change. The easiest way to check whether two trace elements in a suite of lavas follow this rule is to make use of a mathematical transformation that converts Equation 4.9, which defines a curve on a plot of C_1

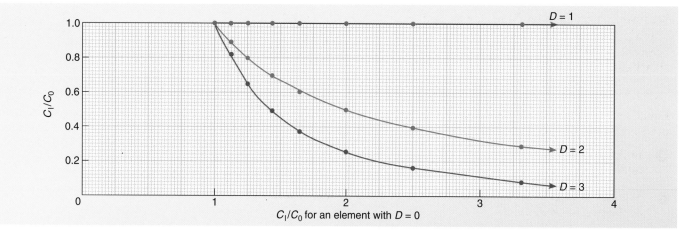

Figure 4.12 Graph of C_1/C_0 for elements with $D = 1$, 2 and 3 (i.e., compatible elements) plotted against C_1/C_0 for an element with $D = 0$ (i.e., a completely incompatible element).

versus C_2, into an equation that defines a straight line. This powerful tool involves plotting the logarithms of the concentrations. The details are set out in Box 4.4, although there is no need for you to become familiar with the derivation of the equations. What is useful to know is the key result, which is that if fractional crystallization has been operating, then a plot of $\log(C_1)$ versus $\log(C_2)$ will generate a straight line. Furthermore, the slope of that straight line is related to the two partition coefficients:

$$\text{slope} = (D_1 - 1)/(D_2 - 1) \tag{4.10}$$

Box 4.4 Trace element trends produced by fractional crystallization, or how to turn a curve into a straight line

Fractional crystallization changes the concentration of trace elements in particular ways, depending on the elements' bulk partition coefficients. If these D values remain constant, then the concentrations of any two trace elements evolve along a unique path, which on a plot of $\log(C_1)$ versus $\log(C_2)$ is a straight line with slope $(D_1-1)/(D_2-1)$. This provides a test for fractional crystallization, as described in the text around this box. The derivation of this useful test is explained in this box.

Consider any two trace elements with concentrations in a magma C_1 and C_2. Let their concentrations in the parental magma be C_{01} and C_{02}. Also, let us call their bulk partition coefficients D_1 and D_2. The Rayleigh fractionation equation for each element is then written as follows:

$$C_1/C_{01} = F^{(D_1-1)} \tag{4.11a}$$

$$C_2/C_{02} = F^{(D_2-1)} \tag{4.11b}$$

To obtain a single equation that expresses C_1 in terms of C_2, Equations 4.11a and 4.11b must be combined in a way that eliminates F. Taking Equation 4.11b and rearranging gives

$$(C_2/C_{02})^{1/(D_2-1)} = F \tag{4.12}$$

Substituting this expression for F into Equation 4.11a gives C_1 as a function of C_2:

$$C_1 = C_{01}(C_2/C_{02})^{((D_1-1)/(D_2-1))} \tag{4.13}$$

An alternative way of writing this equation to isolate C_2 is: Delete curved brackets around "C_{01}/C_{02} in equation 4.14

$$C_1 = [(C_{01}/C_{02})^{((D_1-1)/(D_2-1))}] \times [C_2^{((D_1-1)/(D_2-1))}] \tag{4.14}$$

Because C_{01} and C_{02} have fixed values, and D_1 and D_2 are also fixed, the term $C_{01}/C_{02}^{((D_1-1)/(D_2-1))}$ is also a constant. Likewise $(D_1-1)/(D_2-1)$ has a constant value. It follows that Equation 4.13 can be written in simpler shorthand as

$$C_1 = aC_2^{m} \tag{4.9}$$

Equation 4.9 is known as a power law equation: the concentration C_1 is proportional to the concentration C_2 raised to some power, m.

- In the case of Equation 4.9, what determines the value of the power to which C_2 is raised?

- The power is $((D_1-1)/(D_2-1))$; it depends on the partition coefficients of the two trace elements.

Any power law curve can be transformed into a straight line by taking logarithms of both sides of Equation 4.9:

$$\log(C_1) = \log(aC_2^m)$$

$$\log(C_1) = \log(a) + \log(C_2^m)$$

$$\log(C_1) = \log(a) + m\log(C_2) \qquad (4.15)$$

which has the form of the equation of a straight line:

$$y = c + mx \qquad (4.16)$$

where

$y = \log(C_1)$

$c = \log(a)$

m = slope of the straight line = exponent in the power law

$x = \log(C_2)$.

Thus, a suite of lavas produced by fractional crystallization will give a straight line of gradient $(D_1-1)/(D_2-1)$ on a plot of $\log(C_1)$ versus $\log(C_2)$.

Figure 4.13 illustrates the simplicity and usefulness of this approach. It shows the fractionation trend between Ni and Rb for the hypothetical example considered in Question 4.9. For reference, Figure 4.13a shows Ni plotted against Rb on linear graph paper, revealing a strongly curved trend, with the same shape as the $D = 2$ curve in Figure 4.12. Figure 4.13b shows the same compositional trend, but plotted on logarithmic graph paper. This has the effect of squeezing together the data points at high concentrations and stretching out the points at low concentrations. The result is that the curvature of Figure 4.13a is removed, leaving a straight line — the easily identified hallmark of fractional crystallization.

In practice, we need to plot as wide a range of concentrations as possible; otherwise, we would end up with a very short spread of points and it would be difficult to decide whether we were looking at a straight line or just a short segment of a curve. So, when testing a set of geochemical data for evidence of fractional crystallization, it is best to plot the most compatible element (largest D) against the most incompatible (smallest D).

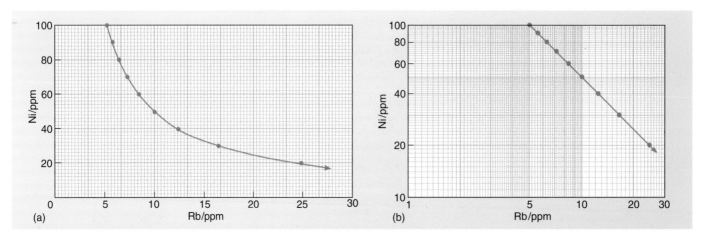

Figure 4.13 Fractional crystallization trend of magmas derived from a parental basalt with 5 ppm Rb and 100 ppm Ni, when $D_{Rb} = 0$ and $D_{Ni} = 2$. (a) Plotted on linear graph paper; (b) plotted on logarithmic graph paper.

An extra result that comes out of the plot on logarithmic graph paper is that the slope of the straight line fractionation trend is directly related to the bulk partition coefficients of the two plotted elements (Equation 4.10).

> Question 4.10 Using a ruler, measure the gradient of the straight line in Figure 4.13b.

The anticipated gradient is, from Equation 4.10,

$$m = (D_{Ni}-1)/(D_{Rb}-1) = (2-1)/(0-1) = -1$$

and this should tally with your answer to Question 4.10. If you obtained a different answer, it is important that you check your calculation of the gradient by referring to the answer to Question 4.10.

4.2.5 Testing for fractional crystallization in the Santorini magma chamber

The patterns of major element variation in Santorini's lavas were suggestive of fractional crystallization having occurred within the Santorini magma chamber (Section 4.2.3). You can now develop that idea further by incorporating information about the variation in trace elements. From Table 4.1, it is clear that some trace elements increase with increasing silica (Rb, Th, Zr) while others (Ni, V, Sc) decrease as the silica content increases. Sr remains rather constant over the range basalt to andesite, but decreases sharply in the most silicic rocks (Figure 4.14).

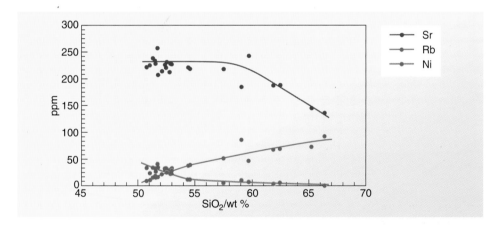

Figure 4.14 Plot of Rb, Sr and Ni versus SiO_2 for Skaros lavas.

Figure 4.14 shows that Rb is behaving as an incompatible trace element, which is consistent with it having K_d values of 0.02 or less for all the minerals that crystallize from basaltic and intermediate magma compositions (Table 4.4). Such very small K_d values result from the Rb^+ ion being too large to fit comfortably within the structures of any of the crystallizing minerals. In contrast, Sr forms a Sr^{2+} ion that fairly readily fits in to the plagioclase structure. The K_d value for Sr between plagioclase and liquid is therefore high and in the range 1 to 5, depending on the An content of the plagioclase. (The K_d value increases as An content decreases because the structure of An-poor plagioclase is more elastic and can therefore accommodate large Sr^{2+} ions more easily than can An-rich plagioclase.) The compositions and structures of augite, and especially olivine and titanomagnetite, are such that the K_d value for Sr for these minerals is much less than 1.

● Would you expect fractional crystallization of basalt, involving a mineral assemblage containing plagioclase, to increase or decrease the concentrations of (a) Rb and (b) Sr in the residual liquids?

● (a) Because Rb is incompatible in all of the minerals that crystallize from basalt, Rb concentrations will increase. (b) Because Sr is compatible in plagioclase but incompatible in the other minerals, whether the bulk partition coefficient will be <1, =1 or >1 will depend on the proportion of plagioclase. If K_d is 2 (Table 4.4), then mineral assemblages with >50% plagioclase will have a D_{Sr} value greater than 1, so Sr would decrease in that case.

Table 4.4 Representative values of mineral partition coefficients (K_d) between minerals in equilibrium with liquids of basaltic composition.

	Olivine	Orthopyroxene	Augite	Plagioclase	Titanomagnetite
Rb (rubidium)	0.01	0.02	0.02	0.02	0.01
Sr (strontium)	0.01	0.04	0.07	2	0.01
Ni (nickel)	7	3	2	0.01	5
V (vanadium)	0.08	0.8	1.2	0.01	5
Sc (scandium)	0.20	0.7	1.6	0.01	5
Th (thorium)	0.00	0.00	0.00	0.03	0.03
Zr (zirconium)	0.01	0.05	0.1	0.01	0.1

On a log–log plot of Sr against Rb, lavas from Skaros show the trends seen in Figure 4.15. The simplest interpretation of this plot is that there are two straight line segments. Because a straight line on a log–log trace element plot indicates fractional crystallization, the data from Skaros can be interpreted in terms of two stages of fractional crystallization. The break in slope occurs at about 50 ppm Rb, implying that at this composition the mineral assemblage (or proportion of minerals) changes so as to increase the bulk partition coefficient of Sr. This is reminiscent of the plots of major element variation (Figures 4.9, 4.10) that indicated the Skaros lavas appeared to be formed by fractional crystallization involving a change in the mineral assemblage at about 57% SiO_2.

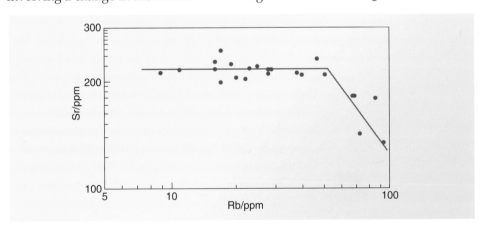

Figure 4.15 Log–log plot of Sr against Rb in Skaros lavas.

Question 4.11 Using the information on K_d values in Table 4.4, what other trace elements can be used to indicate the effect of particular minerals during fractional crystallization?

Trace elements with bulk partition coefficients (D values) that are larger than 1 during fractional crystallization indicate that specific minerals with high mineral partition coefficients (K_d values) for those elements were part of the crystallizing assemblage of minerals.

4.2.6 Fractional crystallization and rare earth elements (REE)

In studying the origins of basalts in Block 2, you touched upon the different behaviours of certain trace elements known as the **rare earth elements**, or **REE** for short. They are also useful for investigating the fractional crystallization of magmas. First, what exactly is a rare earth element, and why should they be attractive to geochemists? The REE have atomic numbers between 57 and 71 (Table 4.5) and share very similar chemical properties. For instance, they all form trivalent ions (although Eu forms Eu^{2+} as well as Eu^{3+}, and Ce forms Ce^{4+} as well as Ce^{3+}) and they have ionic radii in the restricted range 103.2 pm to 86.1 pm (pm stands for picometre, which is 10^{-12} m). REE with low atomic number (and therefore low atomic mass) are referred to as **light REE**, or **LREE**, whereas those with high atomic mass are **heavy REE**, or **HREE**.

Table 4.5   The rare earth elements.

Atomic no.	Element	Symbol	Ionic radius/pm	Chondritic abundance normalizing values/ ppm
57	lanthanum	La	103.2	0.367
58	cerium	Ce	101.0	0.957
59	praseodymium	Pr	99.0	0.137
60	neodymium	Nd	98.3	0.711
61	promethium	Pm*	–	–
62	samarium	Sm	95.8	0.231
63	europium	Eu	94.7	0.087
64	gadolinium	Gd	93.8	0.306
65	terbium	Tb	92.3	0.058
66	dysprosium	Dy	91.2	0.381
67	holmium	Ho	90.1	0.0851
68	erbium	Er	89.0	0.249
69	thulium	Tm	88.0	0.0356
70	ytterbium	Yb	86.8	0.248
71	lutetium	Lu	86.1	0.0381

* Pm has no stable isotopes and does not occur in nature.

Concentrations of REE are reported in parts per million (ppm), just like any other trace element, but are often displayed graphically after being normalized (divided by) the REE concentrations of chondritic meteorites, as in Figure 4.16. Notice that the vertical axis uses a 'powers of ten', or logarithmic, scale because the normalized concentrations of different REE can differ by well over an order of magnitude. The reason for the normalization procedure is to get round the fact that REE with even atomic numbers are more abundant than those with odd atomic numbers (see Table 4.5). By normalizing the REE analysis of a rock, the 'spiky' nature of the REE abundances is removed and replaced by a smooth pattern (Figure 4.16) whose regularity brings out the geochemical coherence of this group of elements. The straight lines connecting individual chondrite-normalized points define the **REE pattern** of each rock. Thus, the REE pattern of chondrites would be a horizontal line with a y-axis value of 1.0. Most rocks have higher REE abundances and so plot above that line — for example, the Santorini lavas in Figure 4.16.

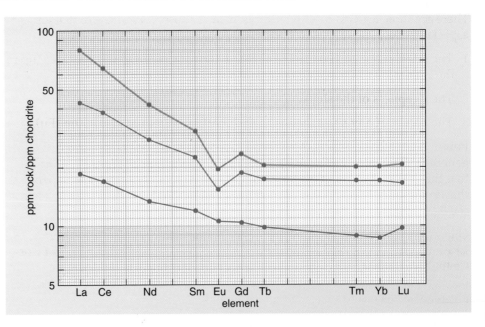

Figure 4.16 Chondrite-normalized REE patterns of Santorini basalt (green), basaltic andesite (red) and andesite (purple).

What can be learnt from REE patterns? What do they tell us about magmatic processes? Look first at just one element, say La, and how it varies from the basalt to the andesite at Santorini.

⬤ Is La an incompatible or compatible trace element in the Santorini lavas?

⬤ The concentration in the most silicic rock is higher than that in the less silicic rocks so, like Rb, La must be incompatible.

All the REE are behaving incompatibly, and this is because their K_d values for most minerals are less than 1. For example, partition coefficients for basalts and basaltic andesites shown in Figure 4.17 are less than 1 except for HREE in garnet. Notice that for each mineral, K_d varies systematically from LREE to HREE, with the exception of europium (Eu) in plagioclase and to a lesser extent magnetite. Usually, the HREE have the largest partition coefficients. When the LREE become enriched by fractional crystallization, the HREE will be only moderately enriched.

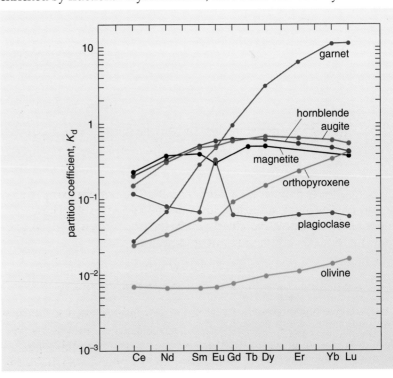

Figure 4.17 Partition coefficients (K_d) of selected REE between minerals and basalt to basaltic andesite liquids.

There are three aspects of REE patterns such as those in Figure 4.16 that are especially useful in studies of magma evolution:

1   The slope of the pattern can be negative (down to the right) or positive (up to the right).

2   The steepness of the slope.

3   The nature of any perturbation in each pattern shown by europium (Eu).

Points 1 and 2 have already been alluded to; fractional crystallization will generally cause the LREE to become enriched more rapidly than the HREE so that the REE pattern has a negative slope. The steepness of the slope depends on the amount of crystals removed by fractionation and the partition coefficients of the fractionating crystal assemblage.

One way of describing the steepness of a REE pattern is to calculate the ratio of LREE to HREE. Specifically, the ratio of the normalized concentration of La or Ce to that of Yb or Lu can be used. The elements Ce and Yb and the ratio $(Ce/Yb)_N$ are selected here, where the subscript N is there to remind us that we are dealing with chondrite-normalized abundances.

> **Question 4.12** What is the $(Ce/Yb)_N$ ratio for (a) the basalt in Figure 4.16, and (b) the andesite in Figure 4.16?

The andesite's REE pattern certainly looks to be the steepest on Figure 4.16, and the calculation of $(Ce/Yb)_N$ confirms this. The $(Ce/Yb)_N$ ratio increases as SiO_2 and Rb increase, with a hint of a change in slope of the trend in Figure 4.18 at around 50 ppm Rb. Doesn't this sound familiar? You found earlier that the bulk partition coefficients of several other trace elements changed at about this composition (equivalent to 57% SiO_2), apparently coincident with a change from an olivine + augite + plagioclase mineralogy to plagioclase + augite + orthopyroxene + titanomagnetite.

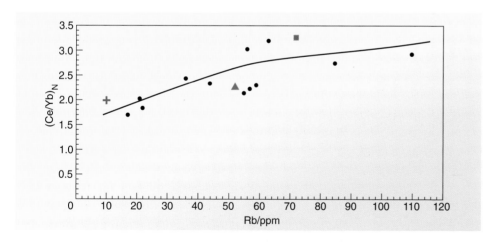

Figure 4.18 Plot of $(Ce/Yb)_N$ against Rb for Santorini lavas. The green cross, red triangle and purple square identify the basalt, basaltic andesite and andesite whose REE patterns are given in Figure 4.16.

Returning to Figure 4.16, each lava has a fairly smooth REE pattern except for the odd behaviour of europium in the basaltic andesite and andesite. These magmas fractionated from basalt, but clearly Eu has not been enriched as much as the neighbouring REE samarium (Sm) and gadolinium (Gd).

> **Question 4.13** Which mineral will provide Eu with an anomalous fractionation behaviour? (*Hint:* think about the K_d values for Eu.)

Europium has an anomalously high K_d value for plagioclase because it can occur as Eu^{2+}, enabling it to enter the Ca^{2+} site in the plagioclase structure (just as Sr^{2+} does; recall that K_d for Sr between plagioclase and liquid is >1, e.g. Table 4.4), whereas Sm^{3+} and Gd^{3+} cannot and are, therefore, much more incompatible. The preferential removal of Eu during plagioclase fractionation will therefore lead to a trough in the REE pattern of evolved magmas, and the mineral extract, or cumulate, will have a corresponding peak in its REE pattern. Thus, the anomalous behaviour of Eu is a very clear indicator of the role of plagioclase fractionation or accumulation in the origin of igneous rocks. The perturbation, either a spike or a trough, is known as the **europium anomaly**. A spike, reflecting plagioclase accumulation, is called a positive europium anomaly and a trough, reflecting plagioclase removal, is a negative europium anomaly.

A simple way of describing the size of an europium anomaly is illustrated in Figure 4.19, which shows the REE pattern of a rhyolite with a negative europium anomaly. Apart from the europium anomaly, the REE pattern is smooth and if Eu had not been one of the analysed elements we would anticipate Eu to plot at a value identified as Eu* (= 21.8), which lies on the straight line joining Sm with Gd. The real value (10.3) departs from this interpolated concentration, of course, such that the europium anomaly can be given as

$$Eu/Eu^* = 10.3/21.8 = 0.47.$$

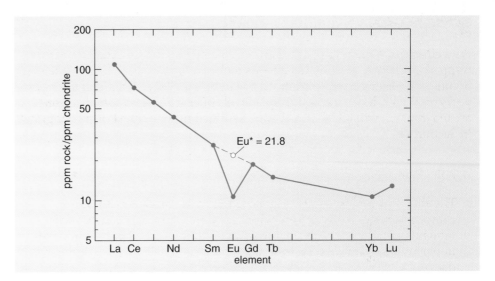

Figure 4.19 The REE pattern of a rhyolite, showing the method of finding Eu* needed to calculate the europium anomaly Eu/Eu*.

Question 4.14 What is the europium anomaly of (a) the basalt, (b) the basaltic andesite and (c) the andesite from Santorini whose REE patterns are given in Figure 4.16?

Question 4.15 What does your answer to Question 4.14 imply about the relative amounts of plagioclase fractionation involved in generating the basaltic andesite and the andesite from the basalt?

4.2.7 Cumulates and plutons

Throughout this subsection, you have been learning about the range of compositions of volcanic rocks — the liquid portion of igneous geology. There are, of course, other parts to the volcanic systems that are found in arcs. These are the accumulations of crystals extracted from cooling magma as they undergo fractional crystallization in subsurface magma chambers to produce the evolved magmas that are sometimes erupted to the surface. These cumulates remain lodged in the crust and cannot escape unless accidentally caught up in magma as it flows from the magma chamber on its way to the surface. Such xenoliths of cumulate rocks are occasionally found, and an example from Santorini is shown in Figure 4.20. These cumulates have the right mineralogy and mineral proportions to be the complements of evolved lavas and primitive magmas:

evolved magma = primitive magma − removed cumulate minerals.

Figure 4.20 Photomicrograph of plagioclase–augite–orthopyroxene–magnetite cumulate from Santorini.

As well as cumulate rocks, plutonic rocks formed by the freezing of magmas trapped at depth also generate igneous rocks within arc crust, though they only become visible to geologists after magmatism has died down and millions of years of erosion have exposed deeper levels of crust. These plutonic records of arc magmatism will be described and examined in the context of crustal growth in Section 7.

4.2.8 Summary of Section 4.2

- The chemical compositions of igneous minerals correlate with the composition of the liquid from which they grew. Thus, ferromagnesian minerals grown from a basalt are richer in Mg end-members (Fo in olivine, En in pyroxenes) than those in less-magnesian magmas such as andesite and dacite. The Mg-number, $100 \times Mg/(Mg + Fe)$, of these minerals decreases as the MgO content of the host rock decreases. Similarly, the more primitive magmas have Ca-rich (An-rich) plagioclase feldspar, whereas andesites and dacites have progressively more sodic (An-poor, Ab-rich) plagioclase.

- Trace element variation in a magma series can be investigated in terms of magmatic processes using the Rayleigh fractionation equation, which describes the effect of fractional crystallization on the concentration of a trace element: $C_1 = C_0 F^{(D-1)}$. Incompatible trace elements (those with $D < 1$) therefore increase in concentration with fractionation (decreasing amount of remaining liquid, F) and compatible elements ($D > 1$) decrease in concentration. Rb and Zr are examples of highly incompatible trace elements in most magmas.

- The concentrations of two trace elements in a suite of magmas produced by fractional crystallization are related by a power law of the form $C_1 = aC_2^m$, where $m = (D_1-1)/(D_2-1)$. On a log–log graph, a power law appears as a straight line, with gradient m. When the concentrations of a highly compatible trace element are plotted against those of a highly incompatible trace element on log–log graph paper, a reasonable straight-line trend will be revealed only if a series of magmas are related by fractional crystallization. The gradient of the straight line is determined by the bulk partition coefficients of the two plotted elements. On a plot of these same elements but on linear graph paper, the trend produced by fractional crystallization is a highly curved one.

- The compatible trace elements in magma series produced by fractional crystallization indicate that minerals with high mineral partition coefficients (K_d) for those elements were crystallizing. For example, compatible behaviour of Sr implies plagioclase fractionation, compatible behaviour of Ni implies olivine and/or titanomagnetite fractionation, compatible behaviour of Sc and V implies augite and/or titanomagnetite fractionation.

- Rare earth element (REE) patterns of arc magmas have negative slopes (e.g., $(Ce/Yb)_N > 1$) that steepen with fractional crystallization. The REE patterns have negative europium anomalies ($Eu/Eu^* < 1$) that deepen with fractional crystallization and are the hallmark of plagioclase fractionation.

4.3   Magma mixing

So far in Section 4 we have found that the Skaros lavas cover a range of chemical composition, and that the composition of the minerals in these lavas changes systematically with rock composition. Furthermore, rock compositional trends, both for major elements and trace elements, are consistent with fractional crystallization in a magma chamber lying beneath the volcano. There are clues in some of the rocks, however, that indicate fractional crystallization is not the whole story.

In some cases, pumices and lavas are found with a streaky texture (Figure 4.21). In the case of Figure 4.21a, the white portion is dacitic in composition, with 68% SiO_2, whereas the darker streaks are andesitic, with 58% SiO_2. The contacts between these two compositions are extremely sharp, as if the andesite was being stirred into the dacite. This is in fact what has happened — the pumice is a frozen specimen of a streaky mixture of two different magmas and looks like a swirled blend of different-coloured ice creams. The sharpness of the contacts between the different glasses indicates that the stirring process must have been interrupted at the instant of the eruption in order for such fine and delicate structures to be preserved. For obvious reasons, such pumice is often referred to as streaky or banded pumice.

The overall, or bulk, composition of the banded pumice in Figure 4.21a must be between 58 and 68% SiO_2. The constituent parts, andesite and dacite, may have formed by fractional crystallization, but the resultant mixture has formed by a different process, that of magma mixing. As its name implies, **magma mixing** is a process that causes two (or more) magmas to be mingled together, forming a new magma of a composition between that of the end-members.

(a)   (b)

Figure 4.21   (a) White pumice with streaks of dark grey pumice. (b) Thin section of lava showing swirled bands of different-coloured groundmass.

The two magmas may come together when one is injected into the bottom of a magma chamber that contains the other magma (Figure 4.22). Like a balloon being filled with air, the pressure in the replenished chamber increases and its surface swells until the point where no more magma can be accommodated without the chamber bursting open, triggering an eruption. If the eruption taps the chamber before mixing has gone to completion, then the evidence for mixing is preserved as intimate mixing structures such as those in Figure 4.21. But if mixing has been much more thorough and all the streaky or banded textures have been stirred out of existence, the only evidence for mixing that remains is chemical and mineralogical.

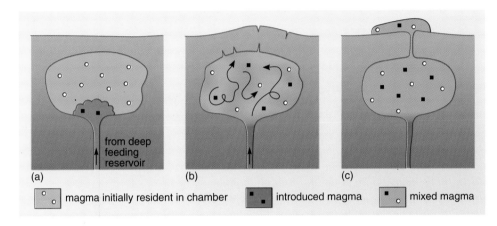

(a)   (b)   (c)

◦ magma initially resident in chamber   ■ introduced magma   mixed magma

Figure 4.22 Cartoon of the addition of magma into the base of a pre-existing magma chamber. (a) Injection of new magma. (b) Pressure within the replenished chamber builds up, deforming the overlying rocks. Turbulent motion in the magma leads to mixing. (c) Pressure is released when the magma chamber bursts open and magma erupts.

4.3.1 Magma mixing revealed by chemical composition

When two magmas with different compositions are mixed together, the resultant mixture has a composition that reflects the degree to which each composition has been diluted by the other. If magma A mixes with magma B to create mixed magma C, then on a plot of any one element against any other element, C will plot somewhere on the straight line joining the **end-members** A and B. If a series of blends are produced, then they will plot as an array of points on the straight line joining A and B. A straight line trend on linear graph paper is therefore consistent with (but does not necessarily prove) magma mixing.

Fractional crystallization produces a strongly curved trend on a graph of a highly incompatible trace element against a highly compatible trace element (when the axes of the graph have linear scales). Magma mixing, on the other hand, always produces a straight trend, so such a diagram offers a way of distinguishing between these two processes. An example is the variation shown between Ni and Rb, which you studied in Section 4.2.4. Figure 4.23 reproduces Figure 4.13a and identifies two magmas labelled A and B. Magma B has been produced by fractional crystallization of magma A, so both lie on the *curved*

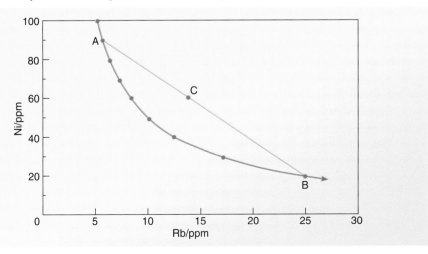

Figure 4.23 Plot of Ni against Rb showing the curved fractionation trend of Figure 4.13a which gives rise to magmas A and B. Mixtures of A and B, such as C, lie on a mixing trend, and this trend lies above the fractionation trend.

fractionation trend. Mixtures of A and B will lie on the straight mixing line which plots above the fractionation trend. For example, mixed magma C contains over 20 ppm more Ni than a fractionated magma with the same Rb content.

4.3.2 Mineralogy of mixed magmas

As well as magma mixing being revealed by certain aspects of whole rock chemical composition, the mineral content of a lava can also indicate whether or not mixing was involved. You found in Section 4.2.2 that the chemical composition of phenocrysts that grew in equilibrium with their host magma will reflect the chemical composition of that magma. For example, a magma with a low MgO content, such as dacite, will precipitate augite with a lower Mg-number than that grown from a high-MgO magma such as basalt (Figure 4.7). If these two magmas become mixed together, then the two types of augite crystal are stirred together and the liquid portions of the magmas become blended to form a new liquid (Figure 4.24). This new liquid will not be in chemical equilibrium with either of the pre-existing augite crystals and these disequilibrium crystals are called **xenocrysts**. The augite xenocrysts become overgrown by a different augite composition that is in equilibrium with the mixed liquid. Similar effects occur with olivine and plagioclase crystals, or indeed any other mineral whose composition is a solid solution series. Thus, the compositions of the cores of xenocrysts tell us about the composition of the magmas from which they grew before mixing, whereas the outermost parts of the crystals have compositions that are related to the composition of the liquid formed by mixing.

Textural evidence in thin section for magma mixing is most spectacularly shown by plagioclase crystals (Figure 4.25). When sodic plagioclase is brought into contact with a hotter calcic magma, the feldspar undergoes partial melting. The edges of the crystal become corroded, developing an intricate sponge-like or sieve texture (Figure 4.25b) that consists of dark glass and clear feldspar. Plainly, this crystal was far from being in chemical equilibrium with its host. However, the magma has attempted to regain equilibrium and the crystal has become overgrown by a rim of clear plagioclase precipitated from the liquid generated by magma mixing. The jacket of equilibrium feldspar protects the interior of the crystal, locking in the chemical and textural evidence of a severe hiatus in the magma's evolution.

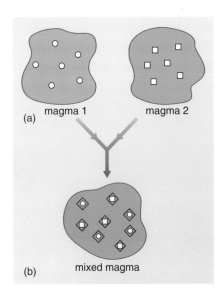

Figure 4.24 (a) Two separate magmas with different compositions contain augite crystals with different compositions (indicated here by different shapes). (b) When the magmas in (a) are mixed together, a mixed magma is formed that inherits both types of augite, and these crystals become overgrown by augite with a composition that is in chemical equilibrium with the enclosing mixed liquid. The rims of all the augite crystals then have the same composition, but there are two kinds of core composition.

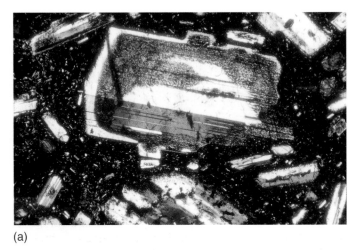

(a)

(b)

Figure 4.25 (a) Photomicrograph in plane-polarized light of a plagioclase crystal in a mixed magma, showing a dark zone, with rounded outline, caused by chemical attack during magma mixing. A clear feldspar rim encloses the crystal, and was formed by equilibrium growth from the host liquid after mixing had occurred. (Field of view is 2.7 mm wide.) (b) Close-up of a corroded, sieve-textured plagioclase crystal. (Field of view is 0.225 mm wide.)

Magma mixing may also involve end-members with different mineralogy. For example, basalt containing olivine might conceivably mix with rhyolite containing quartz. Normally, olivine is in chemical equilibrium with basalt but quartz is not, whereas the reverse is true in rhyolite. So, mixing these magmas together would produce a mixture in which olivine and quartz co-existed; a combination that cannot be explained by equilibrium crystallization and is therefore a good indication of magma mixing.

4.3.3 The case for magma mixing at Santorini

In the basaltic andesites of Santorini, textures such as those in Figure 4.25 are not uncommon. In one example, plagioclase cores have compositions in the range An_{88-73} or An_{65-52}, while rims are in the range An_{70-62}. Cores of augite crystals are around $En_{47}Fs_9Wo_{44}$ or $En_{43}Fs_{18}Wo_{39}$ with rims of $En_{45}Fs_{12}Wo_{43}$. This rock has 54.7% SiO_2, 5.1% MgO, 44 ppm Rb, and 33 ppm Ni.

> **Question 4.16** (a) Calculate the Mg-numbers of the augite cores and rims (Equation 4.2). Then use your answers, with Figure 4.8, to estimate the MgO contents of the end-member magmas in this volcanic rock. (b) Estimate the SiO_2 contents of the end-members using the plagioclase core compositions and the observations reported in Table 4.2.

From this one rock, we have been able to learn about two magmas! One of these is more primitive (higher MgO) than any of the erupted lavas, presumably because primitive magmas entering the volcanic system from below either evolve by fractional crystallization or become diluted (mixed) with evolved magmas. In terms of the rock's chemical composition, its Ni content is relatively high for its Rb content, when compared with lavas without petrographic evidence for mixing (Figure 4.26).

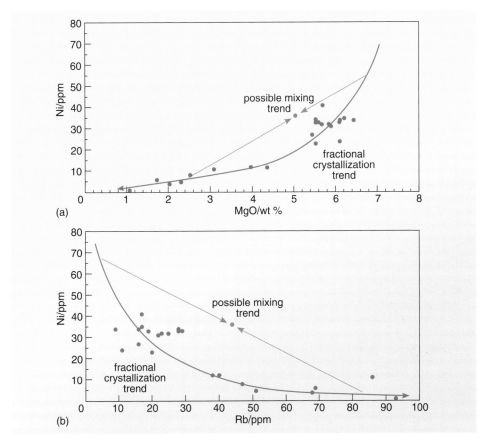

Figure 4.26 Plot of Ni against (a) MgO and (b) Rb, showing that the lava sample with petrographic evidence of mixing (blue) plots separately from the curved fractional crystallization trends and on a hypothetical mixing line.

The evidence for magma mixing, and its explanation in terms of new batches of hot magma feeding into the shallow parts of volcanic systems, implies that volcanoes' plumbing systems are dynamic features. Magma chambers are not isolated vats of cooling magma but potentially complex storage volumes that receive and leak magmas and heat.

4.3.4   Summary of Section 4.3

- Mixed magmas can form within a magma chamber by the mingling of magma already in the chamber with new magma injected into the chamber from below. The influx of magma increases the pressure in the chamber and can trigger some volcanic eruptions.

- The composition of a mixed magma lies on a straight line joining the compositions of the two end-members. A suite of magmas produced by mixing two given end-members in different proportions will plot on such a straight line. For a highly incompatible and a highly compatible element the straight-line mixing trend is readily distinguished from the strongly curved trend produced by fractional crystallization.

- Mixed magmas contain minerals inherited from the end-member magmas. They thus have complex mineralogies such as two populations of plagioclase and augite crystals. These crystals are no longer in chemical equilibrium with the host magma and can become overgrown by a rim of new equilibrium composition. The xenocrysts may also develop disequilibrium textures such as corroded margins.

4.4   Crustal contamination of magmas

Magmatism at subduction zones is responsible for the addition of huge volumes of magma and igneous rock to the crust. The overall thickness and composition of the crust changes as a result. Although primitive basalt magma leaves the mantle and enters the crust, a large range of evolved magma compositions is erupted at the surface, and an equally wide range of intrusive rocks will also be produced. Furthermore, crystal cumulates that are removed from the magmas during fractional crystallization will become lodged in arc crust. Arc magmatism clearly has profound implications for the evolution of the crust, but does the crust have any influence on the magmas' evolution? In particular, is the crust ever melted or incorporated into the hot magma such that crust is reworked into the magmas? To answer this, we need one final geochemical technique; one that can be used for identifying magmas that have become contaminated by crustal material.

4.4.1   Using geochemistry to recognize crustal contamination

The composition of the crust, particularly the continental crust, differs from that of the primary magmas in arcs by, amongst other things, being richer in silica. So, **crustal contamination** would be expected to cause the silica content of the magmas to increase.

- Can you see a problem in using silica content as an indicator of crustal contamination?

- Silica content increases during fractional crystallization (Section 4.2.3), so high concentrations need not be caused by the addition of crust, with the implication that elevated silica concentration is not necessarily diagnostic of crustal contamination.

We need to consider other compositional traits of the crust and how to recognize their presence in contaminated magmas. The average composition of the upper continental crust, relative to primitive mantle, is shown in Figure 4.27, along with the composition of an island arc basalt (from Figure 3.2). Perhaps the most notable feature of the trace element pattern of the upper crust is the high abundances of many of the most incompatible elements (on the left side of the diagram). However, as we have just found out, fractional crystallization will cause the concentrations of these elements to increase as magmas become more evolved, so finding high concentrations of these trace elements in evolved magmas is to be expected, whether or not crustal contamination has occurred.

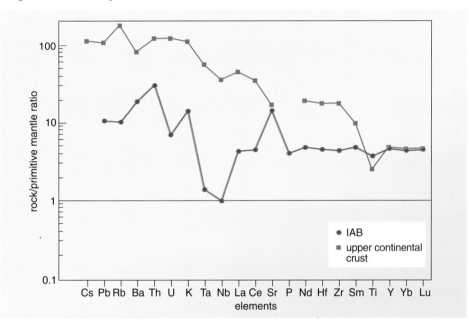

Figure 4.27 Compositions of average upper continental crust and Mariana island arc basalt (IAB), normalized to the composition of primitive mantle.

Trace element ratios

In modelling fractional crystallization, it became useful to consider two trace elements at a time (e.g. as in Figure 4.13) because their mutual variation reflected the process whereby they became fractionated. This is also a useful approach when trying to separate the effects of contamination from those of fractional crystallization. The important result here (derived in Box 4.5) is that for any two trace elements with identical bulk partition coefficients, the ratio of these elements is not changed by fractional crystallization. The only process that can change the trace element ratio is the addition of material with a different ratio.

Box 4.5 Fractional crystallization, crustal contamination and trace element ratios

The behaviour of two trace elements in a magma undergoing fractional crystallization is described by the Rayleigh equation (Equation 4.7):

$$C_1 = C_{01}F^{(D_1-1)}$$

$$C_2 = C_{02}F^{(D_2-1)}$$

The ratio of these two elements will change as a result of fractional crystallization according to

$$C_1/C_2 = (C_{01}/C_{02})(F^{(D_1-1)}/F^{(D_2-1)}) = (C_{01}/C_{02})F^{(D_1-D_2)}$$

According to this equation, the trace element ratio will change during fractional crystallization (because it is a function of F) unless $D_1 = D_2$.

When the bulk partition coefficients are equal, we get the special result

$C_1/C_2 = (C_{01}/C_{02})\,F^0$

and because any number (except zero) raised to the power zero is equal to 1,

$C_1/C_2 = C_{01}/C_{02}$

i.e. the trace element ratio remains constant during fractional crystallization when $D_1 = D_2$.

If we can identify two elements with identical bulk partition coefficients, then the ratio of these elements will remain constant in a magma series influenced only by fractional crystallization (and mixing of magmas produced by fractional crystallization). Variable trace element ratios must indicate the presence of some other material with a different ratio.

To apply this theory to some real volcanic rocks, information on partition coefficients (Table 4.4) is needed to guide the selection of two suitable trace elements. A compatible trace element (e.g. Sr, Ni, Cr, V) together with an incompatible trace element (e.g. Rb, Th, Zr) would not be appropriate because, by their definitions, their bulk partition coefficients will be very different. Indeed, this feature causes a compatible versus incompatible trace element plot (on linear graph paper) to be markedly curved (Figures 4.12, 4.13a). On the other hand, because the difference between the D value of any two highly incompatible trace elements, say those with $D \ll 0.1$, must always be very small ($\ll 0.1$), fractional crystallization enriches these elements at very similar rates. We therefore arrive at the conclusion that *ratios of highly incompatible trace elements should remain constant during fractional crystallization (and mixing of these fractionated magmas) unless the magmas are contaminated by material having a different ratio of these incompatible trace elements.*

On a variation diagram in which two such highly incompatible trace elements are plotted, fractional crystallization will generate compositions that plot on a straight line moving away from the origin. This is because the crystal extract will contain very low concentrations of the highly incompatible elements, so that its composition plots on or very close to the origin. Extraction of this composition drives residual liquid composition away from the origin on a straight line. In order for analyses to plot on a line that does not project back to the origin, some sort of mixing or contamination between materials with different trace element ratios must have taken place.

As an example, Figure 4.28a shows a plot of Rb versus Zr for lavas from the New Zealand volcano Ruapehu (pronounced 'Roo-ah-pay-who'), which rests on about 30 km of continental crust.

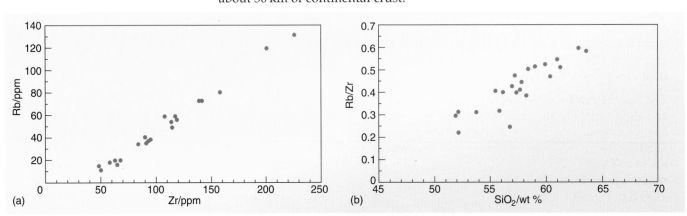

Figure 4.28 (a) Rb versus Zr and (b) Rb/Zr versus SiO_2 for lavas from Ruapehu volcano, New Zealand.

● Are the data in Figure 4.28a consistent with fractional crystallization or with evolution in a system affected by contamination?

● If fractional crystallization was the cause of magma differentiation, then the lavas would plot on a straight line extrapolating through the origin. This is not the case, and high-Zr lavas are enriched in Rb, which is consistent with the addition of a high-Rb component to the magmas.

Because upper continental crust typically has higher Rb/Zr ratios than primitive arc magmas (Figure 4.27), the high Rb/Zr ratio of these New Zealand lavas is best explained by the addition of upper crustal rocks into the magmas before they erupt. Figure 4.28b shows that the proportion of this contaminant increases with increasing SiO_2, so more evolved magmas contain more digested crust. Before trying to explain this in terms of the volcano's 'plumbing system' through which the magmas pass, an important extension to the argument about using ratios of elements with (nearly) identical bulk partition coefficients can be made.

Isotope ratios

The partition coefficient of a given trace element, in a given mineral, depends on the size and charge of that element's ions and the ease with which the mineral structure can accommodate an ion with those properties. If an element has two or more isotopes, then the isotopes will form ions with the same charge and essentially identical size, so their partition coefficients will be identical. In the case of strontium (Box 4.6), the mineral and bulk partition coefficients of ^{87}Sr and ^{86}Sr will be indistinguishable. So, even though Sr behaves as a compatible trace element with respect to plagioclase feldspar, the $^{87}Sr/^{86}Sr$ ratio will not be changed by fractional crystallization (or mixing of magmas produced by fractional crystallization). The $^{87}Sr/^{86}Sr$ ratio of rocks in the continental crust is usually higher than that of the mantle from which basaltic magmas are generated (Box 4.6) so $^{87}Sr/^{86}Sr$ should increase as a result of crustal contamination but remain unchanged by fractional crystallization.

Box 4.6 The strontium isotope ratio $^{87}Sr/^{86}Sr$

Strontium has four naturally occurring isotopes, ^{84}Sr, ^{86}Sr, ^{87}Sr and ^{88}Sr. Of these, the amount of ^{87}Sr increases over time by the β^- decay of the rubidium isotope ^{87}Rb. By convention, the amount of ^{87}Sr is given in relation to the number of ^{86}Sr atoms, in other words, the $^{87}Sr/^{86}Sr$ ratio. Because of radioactive decay, the $^{87}Sr/^{86}Sr$ ratio in any substance containing ^{87}Rb will increase over time. Also, the greater the amount of ^{87}Rb, the greater the production of ^{87}Sr over a given time. Thus, over a given time, a rock with a high $^{87}Rb/^{86}Sr$ ratio will attain a higher $^{87}Sr/^{86}Sr$ ratio than a material with a low $^{87}Rb/^{86}Sr$ ratio.

The $^{87}Sr/^{86}Sr$ ratios of rocks therefore reflect their age and their $^{87}Rb/^{86}Sr$ ratios. As a reference point, the Earth's mantle, which is essentially as old as the Earth, has a low Rb/Sr ratio and a $^{87}Sr/^{86}Sr$ ratio of about 0.703. On average, the continental crust has a much higher Rb/Sr ratio than the mantle (Figure 4.27) but different crustal rocks have different Rb/Sr ratios and ages that range from 4 Ga to virtually zero.

The $^{87}Sr/^{86}Sr$ ratio of crustal rocks is therefore variable (up to 3.6), but values in the range 0.71 to 0.72 are common. The difference between 0.703 and 0.715 hardly seems huge, but the $^{87}Sr/^{86}Sr$ ratio of geological materials can routinely be measured with a precision that is better than ±0.000 02 (i.e. better than ±0.003%), so what might appear on first sight to be paltry differences are actually very significant.

Precambrian crust with high Rb/Sr ratios have some of the highest $^{87}Sr/^{86}Sr$ ratios because it contains a lot of radioactive Rb and there has been a long time for decay to generate relatively large quantities of ^{87}Sr. On the other hand, crustal sediments derived from young volcanic rocks generated in the mantle will have low Rb/Sr ratios and inherit the low $^{87}Sr/^{86}Sr$ ratios of their igneous source. High $^{87}Sr/^{86}Sr$ ratios are therefore indicative of crustal material, but there is no unique crustal value because of the crust's heterogeneous age and composition.

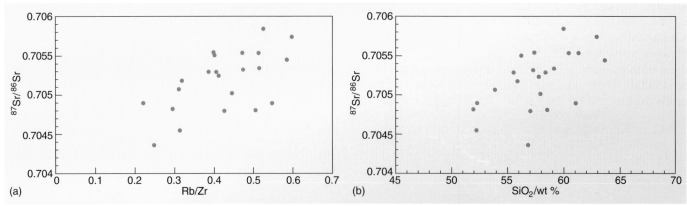

Figure 4.29 (a) $^{87}Sr/^{86}Sr$ versus Rb/Zr and (b) $^{87}Sr/^{86}Sr$ versus SiO_2 in lavas from Ruapehu.

Question 4.17 Plots of $^{87}Sr/^{86}Sr$ against Rb/Zr ratio and SiO_2 in Ruapehu lavas are given in Figure 4.29. Explain why these two plots are consistent with the evidence for crustal contamination that came from Figure 4.28.

At Ruapehu, the magmas that erupt are a mixture of 'fresh' magmas generated in the mantle wedge and pre-existing crust that has been assimilated into the magma. In general, the igneous rocks in arcs need not be totally new crust but can include a proportion of remobilized old crust.

4.4.2 Mechanisms of crustal contamination

We have seen that geochemical evidence can tell us whether crustal contamination has occurred, but this begs the question of how hot magma can melt and digest cooler silicic crust. An obvious constraint that will determine whether a magma can heat and melt crustal rocks is that the magma must be hotter than the melting temperature (solidus) of the crust. This means that high-temperature magmas — basalt at 1200 to 1250 °C or so — will be the most likely to assimilate parts of the crust. In addition, the solidus temperature of crustal rocks depends on the rock's composition, with granitic crust having a lower solidus than basic crust. For example, 750 °C is typical of the solidus of granite, whereas basic crust may not start to melt until 1100 °C. The temperature of the crust before it is intruded by magma will also be important, as it will take more thermal energy to heat upper crust from, say, 150 °C to 750 °C than to heat hotter and deeper crust to the same temperature. Potentially, magma can assimilate crust when it travels up through the crust in dykes and also as it sits and 'stews' in a magma chamber.

The crust beneath a volcano is likely to be a complex volume of heated country rocks, young intrusive rocks, cumulates, and still-molten magma bodies. Much of this region will be cut through by faults and dykes or other conduits through which magmas travel. Different regions may be heated by the magma and melted, whereas elsewhere magma is cooling and crystallizing. Rising magma may melt back the walls of the conduits it uses, assimilating the crust. In a magma chamber or where new pulses of magma intrude and accumulate, crystallization of the magma as it loses heat to the country rocks may be accompanied by melting of any wall rocks with sufficiently low melting temperatures. Depending on the amount of melting and the ability of any melt to be mixed into convecting magma, various combinations of fractional crystallization and contamination are possible. This general process is known simply as the **AFC (assimilation with fractional crystallization) process**.

Magmas that are generated by AFC will show compositional trends that combine those for assimilation and those for fractional crystallization. To predict what such a trend will look like, AFC can be considered as a series of steps alternating between assimilation and fractional crystallization. The involvement of each of these processes can be recognized using changes in $^{87}Sr/^{86}Sr$ and Rb/Sr ratios. To consolidate what you already know about the behaviour of $^{87}Sr/^{86}Sr$ and Rb/Sr ratios during various magmatic processes, answer the following.

> **Question 4.18** (a) During contamination of basaltic magma by silicic continental crust, what will happen to (i) $^{87}Sr/^{86}Sr$ and (ii) Rb/Sr?
> (b) During fractional crystallization, what will happen to (i) $^{87}Sr/^{86}Sr$ and (ii) Rb/Sr?

(a) (i) ↑ (ii) ↑↑
(b) (i) same (ii) ↑

During AFC, all of the effects you accounted for in answering Question 4.18 must occur. On a plot of $^{87}Sr/^{86}Sr$ against Rb/Sr (Figure 4.30), the first increment of crust to be assimilated by basalt (point a) will shift the magma's composition along the indicated mixing line to some point b. The length of the line a–b reflects how much crust has been assimilated. Fractional crystallization of this magma will increase its Rb/Sr ratio by an amount that depends on the difference in their bulk partition coefficients and the amount of crystallization (Box 4.5). In the fractional crystallization step of the AFC process, the magma composition evolves along a horizontal path to point c. A further increment of contamination moves the composition up along another mixing line, to point d, before fractional crystallization changes the composition to e. As the magma evolves it becomes cooler, so the amount of assimilation decreases as the AFC process progresses. In addition, D_{Sr} increases as the magma evolves because the partition coefficient ($K_{d,Sr}$) between plagioclase and liquid is larger in silicic magmas containing sodic plagioclase than in basic magmas with more calcic plagioclase. Sr becomes increasingly more depleted by fractional crystallization as the magma evolves. The effect of lower magma temperature is to cause the contamination steps ab, cd, ef to become shorter. The effect of an increasing D_{Sr} is that the fractional crystallization steps bc, de, fg become longer. The magma can eventually lose its ability to melt its surroundings, and will evolve solely by fractional crystallization (f to g to h).

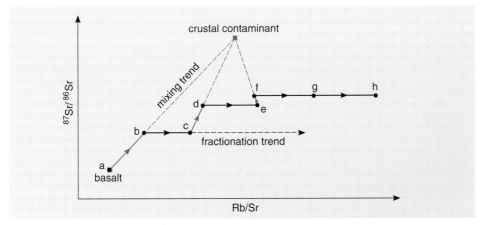

Figure 4.30 The chemical evolution of magma undergoing AFC (assimilation with fractional crystallization) can be seen on a plot of $^{87}Sr/^{86}Sr$ against Rb/Sr. Assimilation (red) produces magmas that lie on straight line mixing trends between the magma and crust. Fractional crystallization (black) produces magmas with increased Rb/Sr but unchanged $^{87}Sr/^{86}Sr$. Alternating episodes of assimilation and fractional crystallization approximate the behaviour when both processes occur simultaneously, as in pure AFC. The sequence of magmas formed (a, b, c, d, e, f, g, h) scatter around a curved trend that becomes flatter with increasing degree of evolution.

Unlike a straightforward mixing line, the AFC trend defined by a smooth path passing close to points a to h in Figure 4.30 is curved. Furthermore, unlike mixing, the AFC trend does not converge on the composition of the contaminant.

Question 4.19 Now look at the $^{87}Sr/^{86}Sr$ versus Rb/Sr plot (Figure 4.31) for the Ruapehu lavas you considered in Section 4.4.1. Decide whether the general trend in their composition fits with simple basalt-crust mixing or whether simultaneous assimilation and fractional crystallization (AFC) is a more appropriate explanation for these lavas.

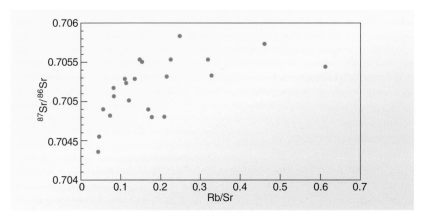

Figure 4.31 $^{87}Sr/^{87}Sr$ versus Rb/Sr plot for lavas from Ruapehu.

This and the previous two parts of Section 4 have shown you how the processes by which a basaltic parent magma can evolve into the array of magma compositions found at arc volcanoes can be deciphered from the chemical composition and petrology of the erupted lavas and pyroclastics. The following Activity allows you to revise some of these ideas through the use of interactive trace element plots.

Activity 4.2   Using trace elements as monitors of magmatic processes

This CD-ROM Activity provides animated examples of using trace elements to identify magmatic processes. It should take you about one-and-a-half hours.

4.4.3 Summary of Section 4.4

* Magma that enters the crust may assimilate those portions of the pre-existing crust with low melting temperatures, such as silicic crustal rocks. Contamination of magma by material with a different isotopic ratio or a different ratio of highly incompatible trace elements will change the values of these ratios in the magma. Fractional crystallization does not change these ratios.

* Volcanic rock series in which an index of crustal contamination, such as $^{87}Sr/^{86}Sr$, increases with increasing degree of magma evolution, such as increasing SiO_2, can be explained by simultaneous assimilation and fractional crystallization in a magma chamber.

4.5 The role of water in the crystallization and differentiation of arc magmas

In the previous Sections, you learnt how certain geochemical patterns or trends in the range of volcanic rocks erupted from subduction zone volcanoes reveal the processes that the magmas undergo during their journey from the mantle to the surface. You have also learnt that subduction zone volcanic suites differ from those of oceanic settings (mid-ocean ridges and oceanic hot spots).

● Place each of the following characteristics in relation to either a subduction zone or mid-ocean ridge setting. (a) Magmas have high water contents. (b) Magmas cover a wide range of silica content and follow a calc-alkaline trend. (c) Basalts are enriched in highly incompatible elements (such as K, Rb, Ba) and are depleted in Nb and Ta.

● All of these traits characterize magmas from subduction zones and do not apply to mid-ocean ridges. (Mid-ocean ridges erupt magmas with relatively low water contents, a restricted range of silica contents, a tholeiitic (iron enrichment) trend, and have trace element normalized patterns which shows incompatible element depletion.)

The trace element patterns and high water contents of arc magmas are produced by water and mobile trace elements being transferred from subducted crust to the mantle wedge (Section 3). The evolution of the magmas generated from this altered mantle peridotite then gives rise to the basalt–andesite–dacite association by the processes described in Sections 4.2 to 4.4. In contrast, decompression melting of relatively dry mantle peridotite yields mid-ocean ridge and hot spot basalts. The presence or absence of water is therefore critical to the conditions under which magmas are generated. Does water also have an influence on the crystallization and therefore differentiation behaviour of basalts?

One way of answering this question is by doing experiments to compare the crystallization behaviour of basalt under anhydrous and hydrous conditions. Several such experiments were completed in the 1980s and 1990s, mainly by Professor Tim Grove and his research students at the Massachusetts Institute of Technology in the USA. They took samples of basalts from the Cascades volcanic arc, ground them finely to a powder and placed a capsule containing a small sample of the powder in a furnace, under controlled pressure and temperature conditions. After letting the material reach chemical equilibrium, the experiment was stopped and the minerals and glass analysed with an electron microprobe. One set of experiments used the dry rock powder and were run at atmospheric pressure (0.1 MPa). In a second set of experiments, water was added to the powder, such that at the conditions of the experiment, the liquid contained about 6% or 4% water (at pressures of 200 or 100 MPa respectively). The results showed clear differences between the two sets of experiments.

One difference is shown in Figure 4.32. Although the liquidus temperature of the experimental liquids decreases with decreasing MgO, as is to be expected in suites of liquids generated by fractional crystallization, the liquidus temperature at a particular MgO content depends strongly on how much water is present. Use this diagram to answer the following question.

● For a given MgO, what is the difference in the liquidus temperatures of dry liquids at 0.1 MPa and wet (c. 6% water) liquids at 200 MPa?

● The liquidus temperature of the dry liquids is about 150 °C higher than the liquidus of wet liquids.

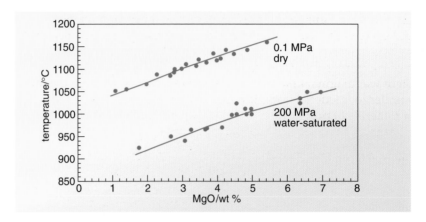

Figure 4.32 Liquidus temperatures of liquids produced by partial crystallization of andesitic compositions in anhydrous experiments at 0.1 MPa (atmospheric pressure) and water-saturated experiments at 200 MPa.

In general, water depresses the liquidus temperature of a magma, but water can also alter the stability of phenocryst minerals such that the order in which different minerals crystallize, and their identity or proportions, are also influenced by the water content. So, in the dry experiments, olivine crystallizes from the most primitive (highest MgO, highest temperature) magma and with falling temperature is joined by plagioclase feldspar and then by pyroxene. This contrasts with wet experiments where olivine, sometimes with the Fe–Al oxide mineral spinel ($(Fe^{2+},Mg)(Fe^{3+},Al,Cr)_2O_4$), is first to crystallize, followed by pyroxene and then plagioclase. The proportion of plagioclase crystallizing increases with magma evolution in both cases, but for mafic compositions plagioclase accounts for over 50% of the crystallizing minerals under dry conditions but only about 30% in the wet case. One result of these differences is on the compositional path followed by the liquids produced by fractional crystallization due to the growth of different minerals as the magma cools. Figure 4.33 illustrates this by comparing the behaviour of Al_2O_3 and FeO_t with decreasing MgO.

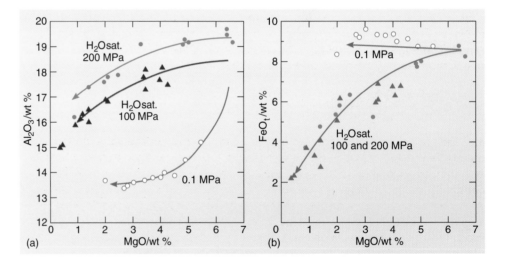

Figure 4.33 Plots of (a) Al_2O_3 versus MgO and (b) FeO_t versus MgO for liquids produced by crystallization of andesites under anhydrous (0.1 MPa, i.e. atmospheric pressure) and wet (100 MPa and 200 MPa) conditions.

Question 4.20 (a) Which mineral has a high Al_2O_3 content and therefore determines whether Al_2O_3 increases or decreases during fractional crystallization? (b) Which minerals have a high FeO_t content and therefore determine whether FeO_t increases or decreases during fractional crystallization?

Early crystallization of plagioclase in 'dry' magmas causes Al_2O_3 to decrease, whereas in wet magmas the delayed crystallization of plagioclase, and the lower percentage of plagioclase in the crystallizing mineral assemblage, cause Al_2O_3 to decrease much less rapidly. Similarly, the lower percentage of ferromagnesian minerals crystallizing from dry magmas allows FeO_t to initially increase with falling MgO, whereas early spinel crystallization and a smaller proportion of plagioclase (and therefore greater proportion of ferromagnesian minerals) prevent a build up of FeO_t. These differences, demonstrated by experiment, led Grove and his colleagues to explain the calc-alkaline (non-iron enrichment) trend displayed by many subduction zone magma suites in terms of fractional crystallization of wet magma. Likewise, dry basalts such as those from the mid-ocean ridges undergo fractional crystallization of a different sequence and proportion of minerals to produce the iron-enrichment, tholeiitic, trend that characterizes magmas from sea-floor spreading centres.

In reality, magma mixing and crustal contamination can superimpose other compositional trends on subduction zone magma suites. Nonetheless, the imprint of fractional crystallization trends anticipated for wet magmas shines through the geochemistry of subduction zone volcanics, whereas mid-ocean ridges and oceanic hot spots conform to the trends expected for dry magmas as seen by comparing Figure 4.34 with Figure 4.33a.

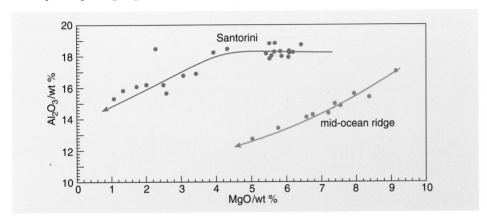

Figure 4.34 Plot of Al_2O_3 versus MgO for Santorini and mid-ocean ridge lavas from the eastern Pacific.

The composition of the minerals that crystallize can also be sensitive to the water content of the liquid, an important case in point being plagioclase. The ratio of Ca to Na in plagioclase that has grown from a magma is proportional to the Ca/Na ratio of the liquid, such that liquids with a high Ca/Na ratio precipitate plagioclase with a high Ca/Na ratio. The constant of proportionality is

$$K = \frac{(Ca/Na)_{plag}}{(Ca/Na)_{liquid}}$$

and the greater the water content of the liquid, the greater the value of K. This means that wet magmas will produce plagioclase that is much richer in the Ca end-member anorthite than the plagioclases produced by dry magmas. The compositions of arc magmas are such that the values of K required to explain the An-rich plagioclase phenocrysts that are not uncommon in arc basalts (see Table 4.2) are at the high end of the range; in other words, high water contents are indicated. This contrasts with MORB, where the relationship between glass and plagioclase compositions are consistent with low water contents.

4.5.1   Summary of Section 4.5

- The amount of water dissolved in a magma can have profound implications for the crystallization behaviour of the magma. Water lowers the liquidus temperature, destabilizes plagioclase and stabilizes spinel. Water also shifts the equilibrium composition of plagioclase to more An-rich compositions.

- Fractional crystallization of wet magma inhibits Fe-enrichment and Al-depletion. Calc-alkaline differentiation trends, typical of many subduction zones, can therefore be produced by fractional crystallization of wet basalt. Tholeiitic trends, typical of MORB and oceanic hot spots, are produced by fractional crystallization of dry basalt.

4.6   Cyclic magmatism: the example of Santorini

The previous subsections have dealt with the chemical and mineralogical signals of the processes that can occur when magma passes through or is stored in the crust. Over time, these processes construct and modify arc crust, and the thermal and compositional interactions between magmas and crust will modulate the size and composition of the magma chambers within the crust and the volcanic edifices produced when the magmas erupt. In Section 2.4.2, you found that Santorini has gone through phases where one style of volcanic activity dominated over others. Boosted by our knowledge of how magmas evolve, we can now return to explore how this volcano's history can be combined with information on magma composition in order to explain any connections between the deep workings of the volcanic system and the infamously catastrophic volcanic activity at arc volcanoes.

The volcanic history of Santorini is summarized in Table 4.6. For the time being, only the general patterns, rather than all of the detailed information contained in Table 4.6, are important. Some of the specific details will become relevant when you complete the Activity at the end of this subsection.

Table 4.6   Summary of the history of Santorini. Prominent explosive eruptions in bold (not in Glossary).

Event	Magma*	Age
Formation of Kameni volcano	D	197 BC to AD 1950
Caldera collapse		
Minoan eruption	**R**	**3.6 ka**
Caldera collapse		
Cape Riva eruption	**R**	**21 ka**
Eruption of the andesites of Oia	A	
Construction of Therasia dome complex	R	
Upper Scoriae 2 eruption	**A**	**79±28; 54±23 ka**
Construction of Skaros lava shield	B, A, D	67±9 ka
Caldera collapse (incremental?)		
Upper Scoriae 1 eruption	**A**	
Vourvoulos eruption	**A, D**	
Eruption of Megalo Vouno; Columbos tuff ring	A	76±28; 54±23 ka
Middle Pumice eruption	**A, D**	*c.* **100 ka**
Cape Thera eruption	**A**	
Construction of Simandiri lava shield	A	172±33; 172±4 ka
Caldera collapse		
Lower Pumice 2 eruption	**R**	
Lower Pumice 1 eruption	**R**	**203±24 ka**
Cape Therma 3 eruption	**A**	
Extrusion of rhyodacites of Cape Alonaki and NE Thera	R	257±31; 224±5 ka
Cape Therma 2 eruption	**R**	
Cape Therma 1 eruption	**A**	
Extrusion of the andesites of Cape Alai	A	456±138; 364±62; 345±88 ka
Eruption of the cinder cones of Akrotiri Peninsula	B, A	522±104; 451±27; 344±24 ka
Construction of Peristeria 3	B, A, D	480±5; 478±3; 464±8; 433±8; 308±10 ka
Extrusion of lavas of Peristeria 2	A	496±16 ka
Construction of Peristeria 1	A	528±23 ka
Eruption of the early centres of Akrotiri Peninsula	D, R	645±92; 619±35; 586±15; 582±24; 553±10 ka

* B: basalt (<53% SiO_2); A: andesite (53–63% SiO_2); D: dacite (63–68% SiO_2); R: rhyodacite (68–73% SiO_2).

The major structural 'events' at Santorini may be classed into two groups. First, there are constructive periods in which lava shields are built by repeated effusive eruptions. Secondly, destructive events are associated with caldera collapse linked to certain highly explosive eruptions of large volumes of magma (of the order of 1 to 30 km^3 magma). Although the total number of deposits from explosive eruptions is very large, and many more have probably been lost to erosion, some twelve very prominent explosive eruptions have occurred on Santorini in the past 360 ka or so (these are identified by bold typeface in Table 4.6). At least four calderas have been identified.

● Information is given in Table 4.6 on the chemical composition of the magmas erupted in each of the listed stratigraphic units. What compositions make up the volcanic units dominated by lava flows, and what compositions characterize the eruptions preceding caldera collapse?

● The lavas fall in the range basalt, andesite and dacite, whereas the large explosive eruptions associated with caldera formation are mainly rhyodacite, with some dacite and andesite.

This pattern is typical of arc volcanoes world-wide because evolved magmas are viscous and, because most of the minerals involved in producing these magmas by fractional crystallization are anhydrous, these magmas tend to have higher water contents. In effect, water behaves as an incompatible component so evolved magmas attain high water contents.

● Is there a general progression with time from primitive magma compositions to evolved magma compositions?

● No. Magma composition changes irregularly, switching back and forth between basic, intermediate and acidic compositions.

However, the most evolved (rhyodacite) magmas are confined to two main periods. These are the 50 000 years or so before the first caldera collapse at *c.* 200 ka, and over the 50 000 years leading up to the Minoan eruption at 3.6 ka. This has led researchers working on Santorini to identify two explosive cycles; the first cycle occupied the period from *c.* 360 to 180 ka, and the second cycle from 180 to 3.6 ka. During the build up to the final eruptions in these cycles, the magma chamber was repeatedly sampled by small eruptions, giving a time sequence of magma composition. For example, the stratigraphy of lavas and pyroclastic rocks in the caldera wall north of Phira gives the compositional history of the magma chamber that fed the Skaros lava shield whose magmas you studied in Section 4.2. The variation in SiO$_2$ content with stratigraphic position is shown in Figure 4.35. Crosses denote magmas formed by magma mixing and dots denote magmas formed by fractional crystallization and minor crustal assimilation (identified from their compositional and petrographic traits using the techniques you studied earlier in Section 4). It is clear from Figure 4.35 that the magma composition fluctuated through time — there is no overall trend towards more evolved or more primitive compositions with time. You can also see that the mixed magmas were erupted mainly in two periods rather than being scattered throughout the sequence. These observations tell us about the competition between fractionation, eruption and mixing rates at the volcano. For example, if fractionation is rapid, then successive eruptions will be of progressively more evolved magmas. This could explain the origin of the sequence labelled A in Figure 4.35.

Fractional crystallization in a cooling, crystallizing magma chamber can occur in a number of ways and can lead to a chamber that is full of homogeneous evolved magma or a chamber with compositional gradients. Left to cool, a magma chamber will start to solidify as crystals grow within the convecting magma and on the chamber walls. Fractionated magmas can then be produced

Figure 4.35 Composition of magmas in stratigraphic order from the base of the Skaros cliff to the capping layers of pumice from the Upper Scoriae 2 (US2) eruption (see Table 4.6 for stratigraphy). Crosses denote magmas formed by magma mixing. Rocks in sequence A become more evolved with time; those labelled B become less evolved with time. The US2 eruption produced a pyroclastic deposit in which pumices from the lower (first erupted) part are more evolved than pumices from the upper part.

by the settling out of crystals to produce cumulates on the floor (in the usual case that the crystals are denser than the liquid). In addition, fractionated liquid is produced by crystallization on the chamber walls, and whether this fractionated liquid stays in place, sinks, or rises depends on any difference in the density of the fractionated and chamber liquids. Like most substances, silicate liquids contract on cooling, becoming denser. But cooling of magma changes the composition of the liquid through fractional crystallization, and this also has an effect on density. As you might expect, the amount of iron in a magma has a strong influence on its density, with iron-rich magmas being denser than iron-poor magmas.

● Do evolved calc-alkaline magmas have lower FeO_t contents than primitive calc-alkaline magmas?

● Yes. This is illustrated by the analyses of Santorini's lavas in Table 4.1.

The compositional effect on density turns out to be stronger than the thermal effect, so with increasing evolution, the liquid density decreases even though it has a cooler temperature. This means that the fractionated calc-alkaline liquids produced by crystallization on the walls of magma chambers will be expected to rise up the sides of the chamber, accumulating under the roof (Figure 4.36). This process has been called **convective fractionation** because it involves convection (i.e. motion driven by density differences) of fractionated magmas.

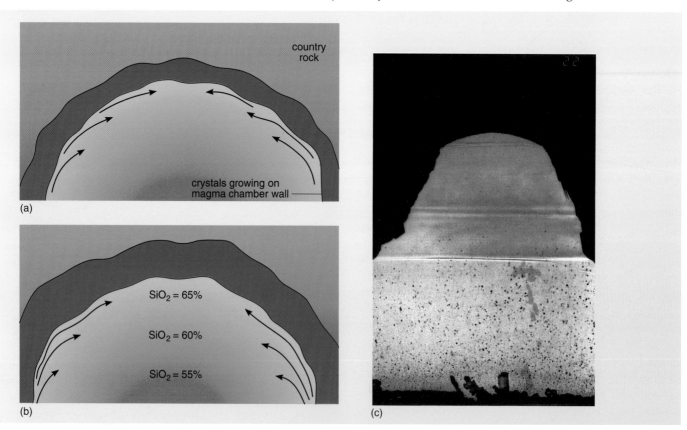

Figure 4.36 (a) Sketch of the roof zone of a magma chamber indicating the rise of fractionated liquids from crystals growing on the margins of the chamber (i.e. convective fractionation). (b) Sketch illustrating a compositional gradient created by convective fractionation in the roof of a magma chamber. (c) Photograph of a laboratory model of convective fractionation in a magma chamber. A solution of sodium carbonate has become saturated on the cold pitched walls of the chamber, leading to the growth of sodium carbonate crystals ($Na_2CO_3.10H_2O$) and the release of dilute sodium carbonate solution. This dilute solution is an analogue of the fractionated evolved magma produced by fractional crystallization. The low-density fractionated solutions form a compositionally zoned region in the top third of the chamber (cf. b). Crystals that have settled through the 'magma' are also seen growing on the floor of the chamber. Total height of laboratory chamber is 30 cm (see Activity 4.3 for more information on this model).

These processes can affect the evolution of magma chambers and therefore the compositions of the erupted magmas in several ways:

1 With time, the volume of fractionated magma that accumulates at the chamber roof will increase.

2 A range of fractionated liquids can be established, with the lightest, most-evolved, liquid at the top, grading downward to warmer less-evolved denser magmas. Such a chamber is said to possess compositional zonation.

3 With time, the most fractionated, uppermost, magma in the chamber will become more evolved.

4 Any primitive magma entering the magma chamber from below will be denser than the evolved magma in the chamber, so the newly arrived magma is likely to spread out as a dense layer on the chamber floor rather than mix with the chamber magma.

The density relationships between magmas can therefore control the dynamics of mixing between magmas and the generation of compositional gradients in chambers. A **zoned magma chamber** can be established by fractional crystallization, roof melting or replenishment by magmas that are denser (or less dense) than resident magmas.

These ideas can help to interpret the compositional stratigraphy of Figure 4.35. For instance, a sequence of lavas that become more mafic with time, such as sequences labelled B in Figure 4.35, could be explained by progressive sampling of deeper and deeper levels of a zoned chamber as each eruption skims off the topmost compositional layer. In such cases, fractionation between eruptions would be sufficiently slow to prevent the regeneration of highly evolved compositions during the intervals between eruptions. In contrast, when the fractionation rate outpaces the eruption rate, successive eruptions are of more evolved magmas, as already noted for sequence A.

Sequences of mixed magmas are likely to reflect times when batches of more primitive magmas were being supplied to the shallow magma chamber from greater depth. Overall, the Skaros sequence displays evidence for episodes of advancing fractionation, exhaustion of a zoned magma chamber and mixing between resident and incoming magmas.

Zoned chambers can also be sampled more completely in very large eruptions, with the first magmas to be erupted being more evolved than later magmas. The Upper Scoriae 2 eruption is an example which appears to have been supplied from a magma chamber containing an upper layer of evolved magma above a lower layer of less evolved magma (Figure 4.35). Santorini's Minoan eruption is another good example, with the great majority of the magma having 70.5 to 71.4% SiO_2 but with some andesitic magmas also being erupted, forming streaky mixed pumices and andesitic scoria clasts. This devastating event happened about 17 000 years after the previous known eruption (Table 4.6) so this long time gap may represent the time required for a large volume of highly evolved magma to build up in the magma chamber. When the pressure in the chamber was released, an estimated 30 km^3 of magma was erupted, destroying much of the volcano and obliterating the township of Akrotiri.

To draw together the volcanology of the Minoan eruption, its relationship with the rest of Santorini, and models for the generation of the cycles of magma evolution and eruption, you should do the next Activity. It involves you working with an extract from the scientific literature and studying the Video Band 'Island-arc magmatism: Santorini'.

Activity 4.3   Observing and interpreting the geology of Santorini

This Activity will take about an hour-and-a-half, but can be done in two halves.

Part 1: A video showing field observations on Santorini and an experiment with a laboratory model of a magma chamber.

Part 2: Integrating stratigraphy and magma evolution, based on reading an extract from 'Santorini Volcano', *Geological Society Memoir 19*.

4.6.1   Summary of Section 4.6

- Magma chambers beneath arc volcanoes such as Santorini can behave in complex manners. As well as evolving by fractional crystallization, they can receive inputs of magma that mix with that already in the chamber, and they lose magma during eruptions. The time (stratigraphic) sequence of magma compositions reflects the interplay between different rates of these processes.

- Evolved calc-alkaline magmas contain less FeO_t than more primitive calc-alkaline magmas. Consequently, magma density decreases during fractionation. As a result, calc-alkaline magma chambers can evolve by convective fractionation whereby fractionated liquids released from the region of crystallization on magma chamber walls float to the roof of the chamber. Over time, a thick layer of compositionally zoned magma can accumulate at the apex of the chamber, with the most evolved (least dense) magma being at the very top. This process can account for the evolved and sometimes zoned nature of the magmas erupted from arc volcanoes after very long periods of dormancy.

- The intrusion of basalt into arc crust generates cycles of volcanic activity and magma composition through the actions of magma crystallization, crustal melting and magma mixing.

Objectives for Section 4

Now that you have completed this Section, you should be able to:

4.1 Understand the meaning of all the terms printed in **bold**.

4.2 Account for the diversity of igneous rock compositions at subduction zones in terms of fractional crystallization, magma mixing and crustal assimilation.

4.3 Outline the differences in magma compositions encountered at arcs in oceanic crust, thin continental crust and thick continental crust.

4.4 Use geochemical models to identify fractional crystallization, magma mixing and crustal assimilation as the main cause of magma evolution, given a set of whole rock chemical analyses.

4.5 Describe the effect of water on (a) the order in which minerals crystallize when basaltic to andesitic magmas are cooled and (b) the generation of calc-alkaline or tholeiitic trends.

4.6 Outline how prolonged intrusion of magma into arc crust, magma evolution and crustal melting can give rise to cycles of volcanic activity and magma composition.

5 Sediment recycling

Oceanic sediment can have several fates, even within a single arc system. These include accretion onto the margin of the overriding plate, subduction with the mafic slab into the mantle, and incorporation into the magma generation zone. This Section outlines the geological evidence for these processes.

5.1 The mechanics of accretionary prisms

5.1.1 Processes in present-day prisms

In Section 2.3, you met some of the characteristics of accretionary prisms and found them to be geologically active regions. There you learnt that once incorporated into the accretionary prism, material tends to remain within the prism and deform, rather than pass through rapidly. Although (mostly sedimentary) material is constantly being added to an active prism, in many cases little sediment escapes — essentially, the whole mass simply churns round above the subduction zone. Direct sedimentation on top of the prism is one way in which material is added to the prism, but what other processes add or extract material from the prism?

Pelagic sediment brought in on the oceanic plate may be stacked up successively at the toe of the prism in a series of thrust slices, as imaged seismically in several subduction complexes (e.g. Barbados, Japan), to form the imbricate stack mentioned in Section 2.3. In other cases, much of the sediment is dragged down along the décollement and stuck to the underside of the prism, a process known as **underplating** (e.g. Makran prism off SW Pakistan). Schematic cartoons of these processes are shown in Figure 5.1.

Pelagic sediment is more likely to be subducted if the sea-floor of the downgoing slab is rugged. Any soft pelagic oozes within topographic hollows in the surface of the downgoing plate are protected by upstanding areas of harder basalt, such that the sediments cannot be sheared off into the accretionary prism so easily. Conversely, in some systems (e.g. Costa Rica) the downgoing plate is

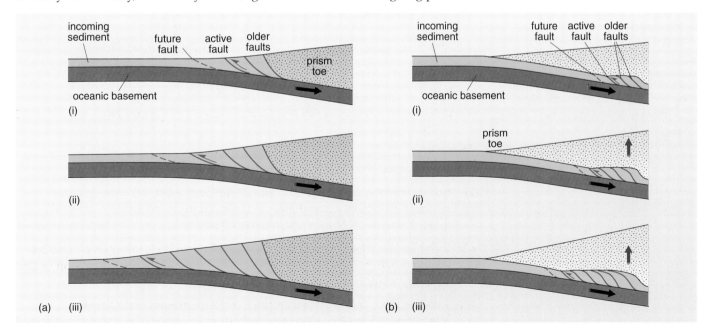

Figure 5.1   (a) Three cartoons ((i) to (iii)) illustrating successive stages in the development of an imbricate stack at the toe of an accretionary prism. (b) Three cartoons ((i) to (iii)) illustrating how sediment is successively underplated to the base of the prism.

so rugged that sediment from the base of the prism is actually scraped off and dragged down the subduction zone. In the Mariana arc, this process, known as **subduction erosion**, seems to be eating away at the basaltic fore-arc (there being no accretionary prism to speak of). In Costa Rica, the rate of subduction erosion exceeds that of sediment addition to the prism, so in recent times the prism has in fact been shrinking (i.e. non-accretionary on Figure 2.13). This has resulted in the prism actually subsiding, and retreating landwards (Figure 5.2).

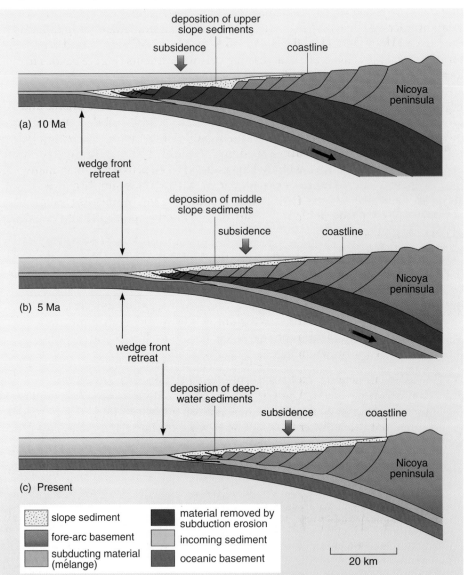

Figure 5.2 Cross-sections of accretionary prism evolution on the west coast of Costa Rica at three different times (10, 5 and 0 Ma), showing how subduction erosion has caused the prism to subside (on curved extensional faults) and shrink dramatically landwards. At the same time, great volumes of sediment have been drawn deeper into the subduction zone system.

Rasping material off the underside of an accretionary prism by subduction erosion would be a very good way of making some of the mélanges found in exposed subduction complexes. However, there are several other processes that can be responsible, and many of them involve fluid, a ubiquitous component in accretionary prisms. A number of factors contribute to high fluid pressures (P_f) within the prism. Much of the sediment is unconsolidated when accreted, and contains significant pore water. In addition, dehydration of hydrous minerals such as clays at depths of 5–15 km adds to fluid in the prism. As the sediment is compacted, by loading and/or tectonic forces, the fluid pressure increases, and commonly approaches or even exceeds lithostatic pressure (P_L: the pressure due to loading of rock). In effect, the fluid in all the pore spaces is forcing aside the sediment grains but, like the gas in champagne, that fluid pressure is confined and cannot burst free until it overcomes the surrounding rock strength.

● What prevents fluid pressure from increasing indefinitely?

● The weakness of the prism itself. All the structures described in Section 2.3 (faults, folds etc.) provide lines of weakness that can be exploited by fluid under pressure trying to break through to the surface. In addition, the prism material is so weak that bodies of fluid can force their way upwards, driven by their own buoyancy.

In detail, the pressurized fluid causes cracks to form, and then widen. These dilatant fractures instantly fill with fluid, causing an immediate drop in local fluid pressure. Minerals commonly crystallize from this fluid in the cracks, forming mineral veins that cut across the prism sediments (Figure 5.3a). The local fluid pressure quickly builds up again, but can also be released when fluid

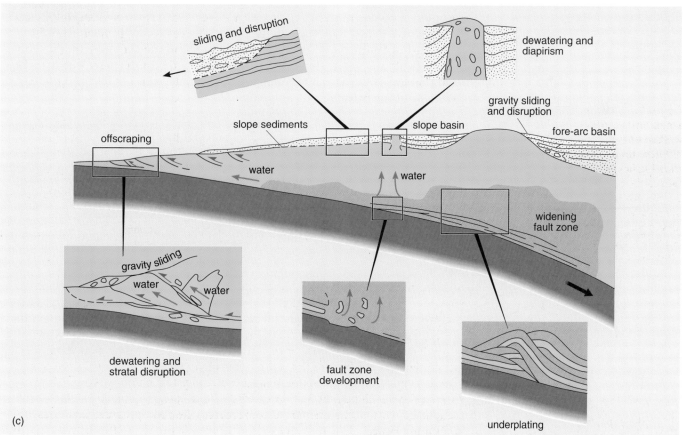

Figure 5.3   (a) Folded prism sediments with veins cutting across the fold structures, attesting to the link between high fluid pressure and brittle deformation. Santa Catalina Island, California. (b) Mélange from Anglesey, with exotic blocks in a highly deformed, fine-grained matrix. (c) Schematic cross-section of accretionary prism showing a variety of deformation mechanisms within the prism. Many of these processes could contribute to the formation of mélanges or olistostromes.

escapes to the surface along faults. More often, the fluid will turn the weak sediment into a slurry, a process known as fluidization, and this slurry will in turn try to escape from the prism. The mud volcanoes mentioned in Section 2.3 probably arise from the eruption of such material at the surface.

Of course, as the slurry forces its way through the body of the prism, it disrupts the surrounding material, tearing out blocks of other rock types and carrying them up bodily towards the surface. Many of the mélanges in accretionary prisms, with their chaotic structure, mud matrix, and varied blocks, are probably the products of these or similar processes. Figure 5.3b is a photograph of such a deposit from the Lower Paleozoic of Anglesey. In some cases, the matrix of the mélange is serpentine mud, which suggests that these deposits originate at least in part from hydrated peridotite in the downgoing slab, perhaps generated in similar fashion to the serpentine that forms the mud mounds in some fore-arc regions. Some mélanges may be the products of vigorous subduction erosion disrupting and mixing various rock types along the base of the prism. However, as you can see from Figure 5.3c, very similar chaotic deposits can result from other processes, mainly gravity sliding of unstable strata at various levels in the prism. These deposits commonly contain rafts and blocks of stronger rock (sandstone or limestone) in a disrupted matrix of mudrock, and provided they are 'of sedimentary origin', they are known as olistostromes. The submarine landslides that form them are mainly triggered by earthquakes, and they are not restricted to accretionary prisms: any seismically active region with weak sediments or steep slopes is prone to gravity sliding. Accretionary prisms, being both very unstable and seismically active, are ideal sites for olistostromes to develop, so these deposits are very common in prisms. Discriminating between a mélange and an olistostrome is difficult, and at times seems more a matter of personal taste!

As outlined above, most active prisms are very weak and unstable, deforming continuously to maintain their shape. In fact, there is a rough relationship, illustrated in Figure 5.4, between fluid pressure and the geometry of the prism — specifically, its taper (the surface slope and the dip of the décollement). The fluid pressure influences how weak the prism material is overall, and thereby the shape of the prism.

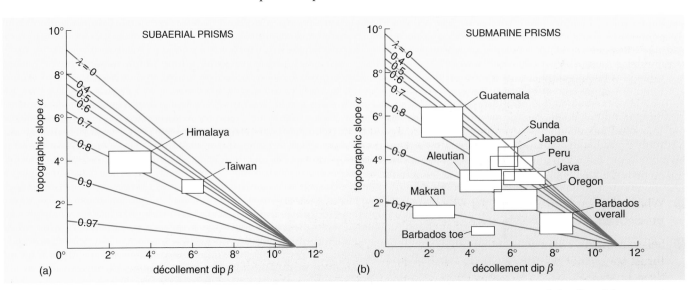

Figure 5.4   Plot of the theoretical relationship between the surface slope α of an accretionary prism and the dip of the décollement β (as defined in Figure 2.15c) as a function of λ, the pore fluid pressure relative to the lithostatic pressure (P_f/P_L). Boxes show measured angles for a number of active prisms.

● In general, what effect does high fluid pressure have on the surface slope of prisms?

● On Figure 5.4, for a given décollement dip, prisms with high fluid pressure tend to have lower surface slopes (they are thinner wedge shapes).

It appears that fluid-rich prisms simply cannot support slopes steeper than a certain value, so they will never build up a steep wedge of material. They seem to be in a state of dynamic equilibrium, with both ductile and brittle processes active throughout. Overall, the prism looks a bit of a mess, but a closer look reveals that parts of the prism are dominated by compression (thrust faulting, folding and cleavage formation), while others are under tension (extensional faulting). Is there a pattern to this deformation? The following two subsections compare some simple models that attempt to explain this dynamic equilibrium.

5.1.2 The corner flow and channel flow models of prism mechanics

The simplest model to explain many of the features of accretionary prisms is that of a simple flow of low-viscosity material in the prism, as illustrated in Figure 5.5a, driven by the drag of the subducting plate. This is the **corner flow model**. The model is inspired by the weak rheology of the prism material, and the observation in ancient examples (e.g., California) of mélanges that include blocks of rocks metamorphosed at depths > 30 km. Although the areas of mélange common to many prisms may reflect corner flow, this process is unlikely to apply to the whole prism. The predicted flow would be so rapid that, for typical convergence rates, the entire upper surface of the prism would be 'resurfaced' within a few million years as material was churned up at the rear of the prism and then flowed forwards towards the trench. Since active prisms have extensive veneers (hundreds to thousands of metres thick, representing several million years of sedimentation in some cases) of essentially undisturbed sediment draped across them, it seems such wholesale return flow cannot be occurring. In fact, in older prisms currently exposed on land there are consistent trends whereby both stratigraphic age and maximum depth of metamorphism increase from the toe to the rear of the prism.

An alternative to the corner flow model suggests that the flow could be confined to a narrow channel adjacent to the subducting plate. This type of **channel flow** requires material of low viscosities, applicable to mud mélanges. Depending on the rate at which sediment is carried into the channel and the capacity of the subduction zone, various patterns of channel flow are possible. Different proportions of the incoming sediment can be accreted by offscraping and underplating (Figure 5.5b,c), while some may return to the surface in a narrow channel (Figure 5.5d). The latter case predicts extrusion of chaotic material and high-pressure metamorphic blocks near the prism toe. Such specific predictions can be directly tested against observations of present-day prism systems.

● What evidence from Section 2.3 is there to confirm or contradict the prediction of the channel flow model depicted in Figure 5.5d?

● Seismic images of prism toes (e.g. Figure 2.15) show coherent imbricate thrust stacks, not chaotic extrusion features. Figures 2.14 and 5.1 illustrate these imbricate stacks schematically, and Section 5.1.1 describes their formation by successive offscraping and faulting of oceanic material from the subducting plate. You could perhaps infer from these diagrams that only rocks from shallow levels, not high-pressure metamorphic rocks, would occur in the prism toe.

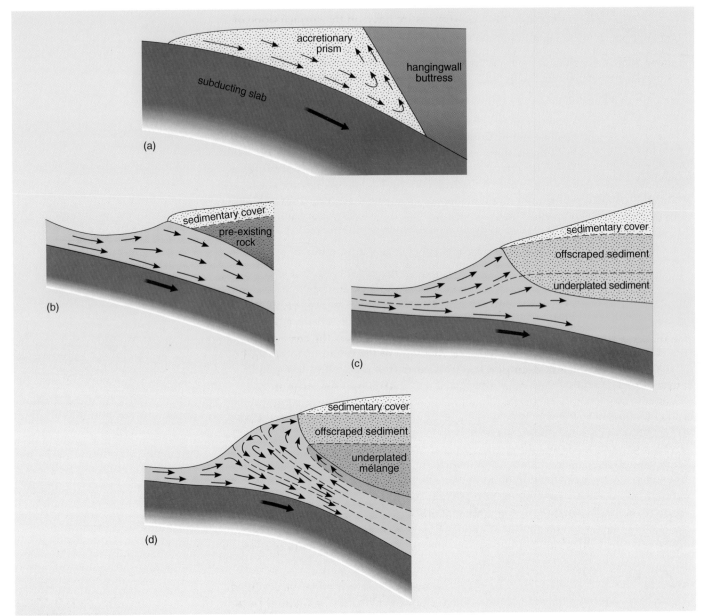

Figure 5.5   (a) Corner flow in an accretionary prism induced by the motion of the subducting slab relative to the hangingwall buttress. Note the distinction between this corner flow in unconsolidated upper crustal sediments, and the large-scale corner flow in mantle wedges above subduction zones (e.g. Figures 2.12 and 3.6b). (b) Channel flow in which all incoming sediment is carried beneath the accretionary prism, to be underplated at depth (as in Figure 5.1b). (c) Channel flow in which half the sediment is offscraped at the toe and half is underplated. (d) Channel flow in which sediment is offscraped, underplated or resubducted within a pattern of return flow.

High-pressure metamorphic rocks are usually found towards the *rear* of the prism in preserved accretionary complexes, not the toe. You will find hard evidence for this in Section 6.2, a case study of an accretionary prism preserved on-land in California. Since the corner flow model is invalidated by the resurfacing argument, and the channel flow model can be rejected by observations in the prism toe, an alternative model must be found.

5.1.3 The dynamic wedge model

A more sophisticated model describes the mechanics of a mass of *plastic* material sliding on a rigid base and confined by a buttress at one end. This is the **dynamic wedge model** and the mechanical concepts on which it is based (analogous to a bulldozer ploughing into a layer of wet mud) can be appreciated by doing a number of simple experiments (Activity 5.1).

Activity 5.1 Simulating accretionary prisms

Now attempt Activity 5.1 in *Workbook 3*. This Activity uses everyday materials to simulate the development of an accretionary prism. It should take you about $1\frac{1}{2}$ to 2 hours to complete it.

In Activity 5.1, you worked towards a reasonable analogue for an accretionary prism, developing a roughly wedge-shaped mass of flour that piled up against a rigid backstop (the card). The flour behaved as a coherent mass of material, rather than as a pile of separate grains like the rice. You may have noticed transverse ridges developing in the flour parallel to the 'backstop' — rather reminiscent of the aerial view of the onshore Makran prism in Pakistan (Figure 5.6). Clearly, the friction of the base on which the flour was sliding played an important part in the formation of the final wedge shape. What other factors determine the form of the prism?

Figure 5.6 Landsat image of part of the onshore Makran accretionary prism, SW Pakistan. There is a strong linear 'structural grain' to this aerial view, caused by successive thrust faults and fold hinges (like the one shown in Figure 2.18) trending roughly parallel to the plate margin. The width of the image represents 50 km.

Apart from basal friction, the most important factor is essentially the weight of the sediment in the prism. This can be expressed by the **lithostatic pressure** at any point, which reflects the weight of sediment overlying that point. This pressure increases towards the rear of the prism, resulting in an overall force towards the toe; it is this outward force that pushes the prism toe oceanwards against the incoming sediment. This force is balanced by the friction (also termed shear stress) along the décollement due to the subducting plate. The

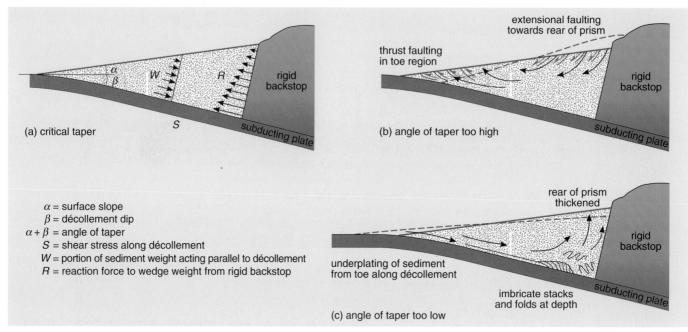

Figure 5.7 (a) Simple representation of the main forces acting within a weak accretionary prism sliding passively on a strong subducting plate and piled against a rigid backstop. There is a unique value of the angle of taper ($\alpha + \beta$) for the situation where the sediment weight (W) and basal friction (S) are perfectly balanced by the reaction force (R) from the backstop. This angle is known as the 'critical taper'. The forces increase with depth in the prism due to the overlying weight of rock. (b) Cartoon of the prism's reaction to overthickening (angle of taper too high). Material will 'collapse' from the rear of the overthickened prism (surface shown dashed) towards the toe in order to reduce the angle of taper to its critical value. The surface of the stable prism is shown as a solid line, and black arrows mark the overall motion of material within the prism during this process. (c) Cartoon of the prism's reaction to thinning (angle of taper too low). Sediments in the prism will compress and thicken to increase the angle of taper back to its critical value. The thin prism (surface shown dashed) is gradually thickened up to its stable geometry (surface shown as solid line).

balance of these forces is shown in Figure 5.7a. The shear stress is in turn influenced by the rate of subduction and the fluid pressure in the prism. For a given value of shear stress on the décollement, there is a critical value for the prism 'taper' (the surface slope + décollement dip, see Figure 5.7a) that ensures the stability of the prism. So if none of these factors changes, and no material is added to the wedge, the angle of taper of the prism will also stay the same even though subduction continues. Deformation in the prism occurs when its angle of taper diverges from this critical value, as illustrated simply by Figure 5.7b, c.

One interesting consequence of the prism's response to a low angle of taper (Figure 5.7c) is that rocks in the deepest part of the prism are brought up towards the surface at the rear of the sediment pile, near the backstop. They will eventually be exposed, either by erosion or perhaps by later extensional faulting. One effect of this motion of rock through the prism is that the trends of stratigraphic age and depth of metamorphism from toe to rear will mimic those seen in preserved ancient prisms. Young, virtually unmetamorphosed sediments will occur at the toe, and progressively older, more metamorphosed rocks will be exposed towards the back of the prism. This tectonic movement of rocks from great depth to exposure at the surface is known as **exhumation**. It is important because, although plate tectonic theory may seem to be dominated by horizontal motions, the presence at the surface of bodies of metamorphic rock from great depths demonstrates the significance of vertical motions.

● What fundamental processes, apart from internal deformation, could change the angle of taper in an accretionary prism?

● Both the addition of material to the prism, and the removal of material from the prism, will tend to affect the angle of taper, particularly if the addition or removal occurs in one part of the prism only — as is usually the case.

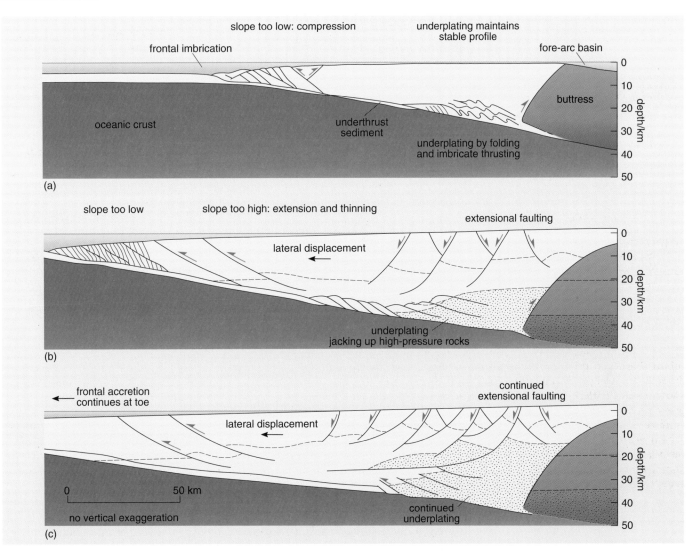

Figure 5.8   Three stages in the evolution of a dynamic accretionary prism. (a) Initial compression results in imbrication at the toe of the prism, and underplating at its base, to form the original prism. A balance could theoretically be achieved between frontal imbrication and underplating towards the rear, thus maintaining the critical taper (at least for the bulk of the prism). (b) If underplated material at the rear of the prism makes the surface slope (and thus the angle of taper) too high, that part of the prism will extend, resulting in normal faults along the top of the prism towards the rear. Note that compressional thrust imbrication can occur simultaneously at the prism toe, where sediment is being continuously accreted. High pressure rocks (stippled) metamorphosed at depth are being jacked up by underplated material at the rear of the prism. (c) If the situation in (b) continues, the combination of thrusting at depth and upper-level extensional faulting at the rear of the prism results in the gradual movement of underplated rocks from depth upwards towards the surface (exhumation). The overall effect is to shift material on curved faults from the overthickened rear of the prism towards the thinner front portion, and thus even out the angle of taper.

Figure 5.8 illustrates in more detail how the angle of taper is liable to change as a typical accretionary prism develops, and how the dynamic wedge model predicts the prism itself will react to these changes. Some of the structures by which the prism adjusts its form are illustrated to demonstrate their roles in the process.

● What effects will accretion of material to the different parts of the prism have on the taper?

● Frontal accretion will tend to lower the taper (the prism will become longer and thinner). Underplating and prism-top sedimentation, which tend to occur towards the rear of the prism, will increase the taper (fatter prism).

● How will the prism react in each case when the taper is altered?

● When the angle of taper becomes too low, folding and thrust faulting occur within the prism. These act to shorten and thicken the prism back to the critical taper angle. For angles of taper that are too high, extension must act to thin the prism — hence the extensional faults often seen on the upper surface of the prism. These changes are illustrated in Figure 5.7.

The latter case, when a prism becomes overthickened and collapses under its own weight, can be likened to a blob of syrup spreading out on a plate. The syrup is so weak it can only sustain a certain thickness. This analogy, which lacks the asymmetry introduced by subduction, has been applied to overthickened mountain belts, a concept explored in Block 4.

> **Question 5.1** Select from the following list the pieces of geological evidence that do *not* corroborate specific predictions of the dynamic wedge model:
> (i)   imbricate thrusts and folds within actively accreting prism toes;
> (ii)   presence of extensional faults on the prism upper surface;
> (iii)   exhumation of high-pressure metamorphic rocks from depth to the toe region of the prism;
> (iv) · overall prism surface profile and tapered geometry;
> (v)   exhumation coeval with continuing convergence;
> (vi)   exhumation of high-pressure rocks from depth to the surface near the rear of the prism;
> (vii)   the occurrence of mud volcanoes in onshore prisms;
> (viii) the progression of increasing stratigraphic ages and depth of metamorphism from the toe to the rear of preserved, mature prisms.

From your answers to Question 5.1, it should be clear that the dynamic wedge model is a better approximation than the corner flow or channel flow models. The majority of the geological evidence to hand can be explained by the model, and even the phenomena that are not specifically predicted by the model are not excluded by it either. In addition, dynamic wedge theory accommodates simultaneous compression at the toe and extension at the rear of the prism, a commonly observed situation. Section 6 further evaluates these two models in relation to the geology of California, where an accretionary prism is preserved largely on-land.

5.2 Escaping the accretionary prism — tracking a sediment component in arc magmas

You have seen that through the action of subduction, convergent plate boundaries can trap large volumes of sediment to construct accretionary prisms. But there is also scope for some of this sediment to be subducted into the mantle, either to be incorporated into magmas and recycled to form part of new igneous crustal rocks or to become permanently absorbed into the mantle (Figure 5.9). Is subducted sediment ever returned to the crust and recycled by arc magmas?

To identify the presence of any foreign component in a mantle-derived magma requires the foreign component to have some compositional feature that is radically different from that encountered in uncontaminated mantle. Furthermore, the added component must behave incompatibly during magma generation, otherwise it will not show up in the magmas but remain behind in the residue. As in studies of crustal contamination, the chemical labels for the exotic component (subducted sediment in this case) are provided by incompatible trace elements and isotopes.

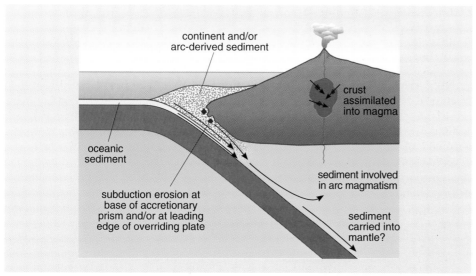

continent and/or
arc-derived sediment

crust
assimilated
into magma

oceanic
sediment

subduction erosion at
base of accretionary
prism and/or at leading
edge of overriding plate

sediment involved
in arc magmatism

sediment
carried into
mantle?

Figure 5.9 Sketch showing possible ways of incorporating crustal sediments and rocks into arc magmas, and hence into arc-modified crust.

The sediments that may enter a subduction zone can be of several types. They range from siliceous and carbonate oozes formed on the deep sea-floor to silty and sandy beds derived from weathered crustal rocks (including igneous rocks produced by arc magmatism) and deposited from turbidity currents. Inevitably, these sediments are compositionally heterogeneous, so there will always be some uncertainty as to the composition of the subducted sediment layer in any one place, and thus a unique chemical tracer would seem to be elusive. You also know from Section 4.4 that crustal rocks can be assimilated into magmas within the crust. Answering the 'simple' question posed in the first paragraph requires the ability to distinguish crustal material that entered the mantle roots of volcanic systems via subducted sediment from that which was assimilated within the crust beneath volcanoes (Figure 5.9). The most conclusive tracer of subducted sediment would be an element (or isotope) that is present in subducted sediment but absent from the mantle and crust. The presence of such an element in an erupted magma could only be explained if subducted sediment was involved in the generation of that magma's parental magma.

In the way that medical scientists can tag compounds and trace their interaction with the human body, or hydrologists can add passive dyes to waterbodies and study their dispersion, geochemists seek a way of tagging sediment that enters a subduction zone and following where it goes. In an ideal and magical world, it would be possible to deposit a large amount of some element or isotope in the sediment layer in a subduction zone and then wait to see how much of the tracer re-emerged in the arc volcanoes.

> **Question 5.2** How long will it take a subducting slab sinking at $5 \, cm \, yr^{-1}$ to reach a magma generation zone at a depth of 150 km?

Much as we might like to do this experiment, we are short of time — but help is at hand from nature. The naturally occurring tracer is a radioactive isotope that is continually formed in the atmosphere, is deposited on the Earth's surface but decays slowly enough that it can survive the journey from oceanic trench to magma generation zone and from magma generation zone to surface. This is the isotope **beryllium-10** (^{10}Be) and it is formed in the atmosphere by the collision of cosmic rays with nuclei of N and O. Rain then transfers the ^{10}Be to the Earth's surface where it partitions very strongly onto sediments and soils. The concentrations of ^{10}Be in pelagic sediments are in the order of only 5×10^9 atoms per gram of sediment. Although this is an exceedingly tiny amount, it is still several thousand times greater than the minimum detectable amounts. ^{10}Be decays with a half-life of 1.5×10^6 years, so that mantle and crustal rocks more

process - spallation.

^{10}Be = cosmogenic isotope.

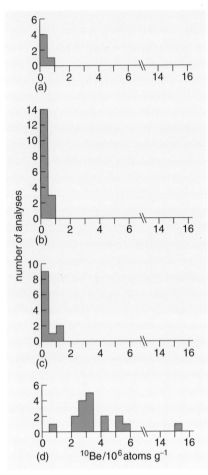

Figure 5.10 Histograms of ^{10}Be contents of lavas from (a) mid-ocean ridges, (b) hot spots, (c) Mariana arc and (d) Aleutian arc.

than 10^7 years old (10 Ma) will have negligible ^{10}Be contents. The presence of ^{10}Be in a lava sample that is uncontaminated by weathering processes should indicate the presence of 'recently' subducted sediment in the magma's petrogenesis.

Figure 5.10 is a histogram of ^{10}Be concentrations measured in volcanic rocks from mid-ocean ridges, hot spots and arcs. Mid-ocean ridge and hot spot lavas have less than 10^6 atoms of ^{10}Be per gram of sample. This tiny amount is indistinguishable from measurements made on Be-free control samples and can thus be taken to imply magma generation in a region of the mantle that is free from (recent) additions of sediment. Higher values are found only in arc magmas, although not all arc magmas necessarily give high values. For example, lavas from the Mariana arc in the western Pacific have ^{10}Be of approximately 10^6 atoms per gram, whereas those from the Aleutians in the northern Pacific give up to 15×10^6 atoms per gram. At least in the latter case there is unequivocal evidence that young sediment has been subducted to the depths of magmagenesis and been incorporated into arc magma.

5.3 Summary of Section 5

- Sediment addition to accretionary prisms occurs in three ways: frontal accretion by imbricate thrusting, underplating to the base of the prism, and prism-top sedimentation. Material may be extracted from the prism by subduction erosion.

- Limited exchange of material occurs across the basal décollement: either entrainment of oceanic basement into the base of the prism, or subduction erosion of basal prism sediments.

- Fluid pressure is generally high in accretionary prisms, weakening the sediment pile and influencing the shape of the prism as a whole.

- Fluid escape can form mélanges, but these deposits may also result from subduction erosion and other processes. Superficially similar olistostromes are produced by disruption of soft sediments during slumping.

- Corner flow is unlikely to occur throughout the prism, though localized channel flow may give rise to mélange deposits observed at the surface.

- Current models for prism mechanics are based on a layer of deformable (plastic) material sliding on a rigid base, and confined by a rigid buttress.

- The dynamic wedge model accounts for the exhumation of rocks from depth to the surface at the rear of the prism.

- Dynamic wedge theory predictions match most geological and geophysical observations of modern and ancient accretionary prisms, notably the tapered geometry, and the deformational response to changes in the prism taper.

- ^{10}Be is an isotope that is produced by cosmic ray bombardment in the Earth's atmosphere and deposited on the surface in rain, so its presence in certain arc magmas signifies the subduction of surface sediment into those magma's generation zones.

Objectives for Section 5

Now that you have completed this Section, you should be able to:

5.1   Understand the meaning of all the terms printed in **bold**.

5.2   Describe the ways in which material can be added to, and extracted from, the accretionary prism, and the potential destinations for components of that sediment.

5.3   Describe physical processes occurring in present-day accretionary prisms, and summarize the direct and indirect evidence for those processes.

5.4   Describe the role played by fluid in the accretionary prism, and features associated with high fluid pressure.

5.5   Describe and evaluate models that attempt to explain the mechanics of accretionary prisms.

5.6   Muster the evidence for recycling of sediment through subduction zones, notably the use of the isotope ^{10}Be as a tracer of young sediment.

6 Terrane accretion at arc margins

So far, you have examined some of the processes by which the continents can grow at destructive margins. This Section introduces the large-scale tectonic aspects of accretion, using two regional case studies of contrasting accreted terranes.

There are two parts to Section 6, covering two different styles of terrane accretion. The first describes the geological history of western Colombia (South America), and looks at the nature and origin of the accreted terranes as a contrast to the gradual accumulation of material in accretionary prisms. The second builds on your knowledge of accretionary prisms from Block 1 and Sections 2 and 5 of this Block, using coastal California as an example of an accretionary prism that has been emplaced onto the continental margin, and is thus accessible to detailed study.

6.1 Transcurrent terrane accretion

Earlier in this Block, you saw how material can be added continuously to an arc system in the form of a largely sedimentary prism. Before returning to that mode of accretion, you will discover how entire blocks of crust can be incorporated at convergent margins. This type of terrane accretion was briefly addressed in Block 1, Section 1.4, with respect to both western North America and Timor.

6.1.1 Geology of western Colombia

Four linear mountain belts (cordillera), trending roughly N–S parallel to the coast, reflect the underlying geology of western Colombia (Figure 6.1). The complex Eastern Cordillera represents the extreme north-western margin of the South American **craton**. The highest belt (up to 5800 m in elevation) is the Central Cordillera, comprising mainly Mesozoic granodiorite and granite **plutons** intruding older basement. This zone is also the main site of post-Miocene andesitic volcanism, i.e. the active arc. The Romeral Fault Zone bounds the Central Cordillera on its western margin. To the west of the Fault Zone is a region with strikingly different geology, dominated by rocks characteristic of ocean crust: basalts, gabbros and some ultramafic rocks. The Cauca–Patia Fault Zone (Figure 6.1) separates thick, terrigenous Tertiary sediments deposited in the Cauca–Patia graben in the east from marine sediments in the west. Basement rocks exposed in the Western and Coastal Cordillera are mainly altered ocean-floor basalts, their ages becoming younger towards the coast. The geology of this region is summarized in Table 6.1.

Table 6.1 Summary of the geology of Colombia from the Eastern Cordillera westwards to the coast, highlighting the variation in igneous and sedimentary rocks and the timing of intrusions across the linear cordillera.

Region	Crystalline basement	Sedimentary rocks
Eastern Cordillera	Precambrian and Paleozoic igneous & metamorphic rocks	various pre-Tertiary; terrigenous Tertiary
Central Cordillera	Mesozoic high-level calc-alkaline plutons intruding Paleozoic schists	(few sediments)
Cauca–Patia graben	Late Jurassic to early Cretaceous basalts, gabbros; intruded by granitoid plutons	terrigenous, Tertiary–Quaternary
Western Cordillera	Mid–Late Cretaceous ocean-floor basalts intruded by Tertiary calc-alkaline plutons	marine, Mid–Late Cretaceous
Coastal Cordillera & Pacific Plain	Late Cretaceous to Eocene ocean-floor basalts	marine, Tertiary

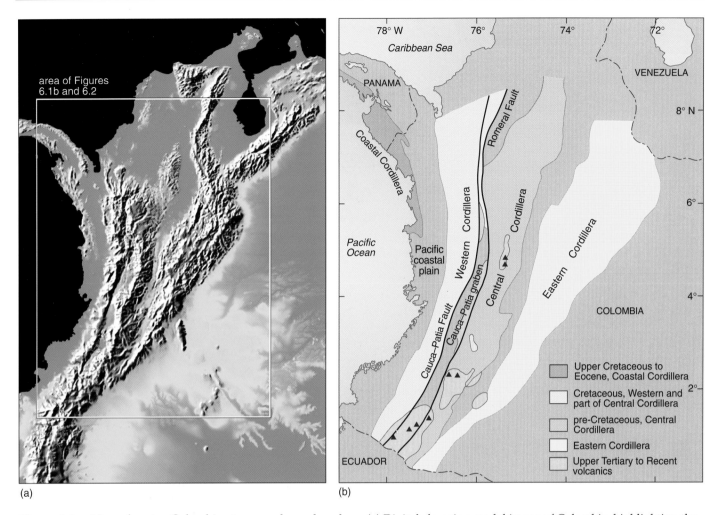

Figure 6.1 Maps showing Colombian topography and geology. (a) Digital elevation model image of Colombia, highlighting the main mountain ranges (cordillera) that run the length of the country, and other major topographic divisions. (b) Geological sketch map of the region, including major fault systems.

● Does the geology change more on an E–W or N–S transect?

● E–W, both in terms of rock type and geological age.

● Do the oldest rocks become generally younger or older from east to west?

● Younger — from Precambrian in the Eastern Cordillera to Late Cretaceous in the Coastal Cordillera.

Question 6.1 Consider an E–W traverse across Colombia (Figures 6.1 and 6.2, and Table 6.1). (a) What major change occurs in the nature of the basement rocks? (b) Do the ages of plutonic rocks change, and if so, how?

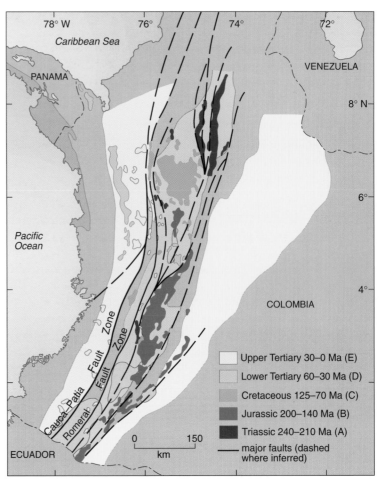

Figure 6.2 Map showing the outcrops of plutons within Colombia, overlain on the geological sketch map of Figure 6.1b. Pluton ages fall into five groups, labelled A to E in chronological order for ease of reference.

6.1.2 Terrane accretion in western Colombia

The Romeral Fault Zone is clearly a major lineament, separating pre-Mesozoic crystalline basement in the east from younger oceanic crust in the west. Furthermore, a geophysical traverse from east to west across the fault shows a dramatic change in the Bouguer gravity anomaly from strongly negative to positive.

- Does this support or contradict the geological evidence above?

- The gravity data support the geology: negative anomalies imply relatively buoyant continental crust (in the east) whereas positive anomalies point to dense oceanic crust to the west of the Romeral Fault Zone.

The evidence suggests that the Jurassic–Cretaceous oceanic crust underlying the Cauca-Patia graben sediment fill is an exotic terrane (known as the Amaime Terrane), accreted to South America along the Romeral Fault. This fault, like the San Andreas Fault, has been dominated by strike–slip movement; it even has the same overall sense of motion (right lateral). Provided that motion has been consistent throughout its history, it implies that the Amaime Terrane slid northwards on a trend slightly oblique to the former margin of Colombia, before finally docking. How can we pin down when this block of crust actually docked?

The key to this puzzle is to find out when the fault moved: this time will be bracketed by the *youngest* basement cut by the fault (maximum age), and the *oldest* pluton that was intruded across the fault but not displaced by it (minimum age). Radiometric dates on plutons are summarized on Figure 6.2, simplified into five stages, A–E.

⬤ What is the date of the oldest pluton that cuts the Romeral Fault on Figure 6.2?

⬤ Cretaceous (125–70 Ma). In fact, the oldest pluton that cuts the fault is Lower Cretaceous in age (dated at 124±6 Ma).

Since the oceanic crust of the Amaime Terrane, also partly of Lower Cretaceous age, must have formed before docking, the emplacement is well constrained, at around 125–130 Ma. In addition, high-pressure metamorphism of part of the Amaime Terrane, thought to record its burial during the late stages of emplacement, has been dated to 129–105 Ma. Dating the accretion of the younger Western and Coastal Cordillera Terranes, however, is more difficult. Dolerite and chert clasts from deformed lowermost Paleocene (*c.* 60 Ma) sediments in the west of the Cauca–Patia graben are interpreted as having a unique source: the Western Cordillera. This suggests that the Western Cordillera Terrane was nearby at the time of deposition, but also that the Cauca–Patia Fault Zone was still active — evidence for the final stages of docking.

From the detail of these examples of terrane accretion, we move on to consider the regional causes and mechanisms of this apparent paradox: crustal *growth* at a *destructive* margin.

6.1.3 Causes of terrane accretion

In contrast to much of the Andean margin, which is discussed in Section 7, western Colombia and Ecuador have undergone crustal growth via a complex interplay of strike–slip block emplacement and subduction-related magmatism. For instance, there is evidence for arc magmatism in the Amaime Terrane directly after accretion, *c.* 105–95 Ma, but not during its emplacement along the Romeral Fault.

⬤ Would you expect strike–slip terrane displacement to result in the initiation of a volcanic arc?

⬤ No. Arc generation requires subduction, and in most volcanic arcs with active magmatism today the subducting plate approaches the plate margin at a fairly high convergence angle (>25° as we saw in Section 2.1.1).

This suggests that the Amaime Terrane first experienced a period of oblique accretion without arc magmatism, followed by a phase of higher angle convergence and subduction with arc-style magmatic activity. In fact, studies in western Colombia and Ecuador have revealed a complex mosaic of basalt terranes and small, isolated segments of volcanic arc, suggesting that switches between transcurrent accretion and subduction happened frequently.

⬤ What might have caused these dramatic shifts in tectonic accretion style?

⬤ The simplest explanation is that each shift from oblique to head-on convergence (and *vice versa*) was a result of abrupt changes in the direction of plate motion in the vicinity.

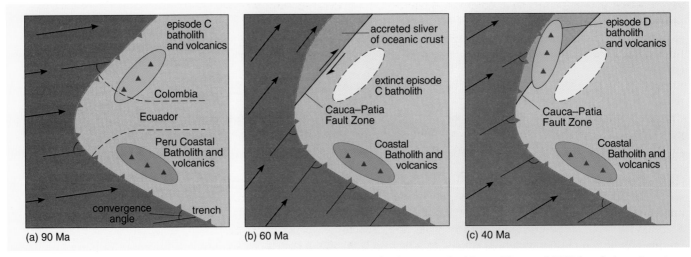

Figure 6.3   Cartoons showing the effects of different convergence angles between the Nazca Plate and NW South America at three stages in the tectonic evolution: (a) 90 Ma; (b) 60 Ma; (c) 40 Ma.

This was the explanation proposed by British Geological Survey scientists working in Colombia for this gaggle of accreted terranes, and is illustrated simply in Figure 6.3.

At 90 Ma (Figure 6.3a), high convergence angles result in subduction and arc magmatism (e.g. Central Cordillera plutons in Colombia, episode C in Figure 6.2). By 60 Ma (Figure 6.3b), the relative motion vector of the oceanic plate had changed markedly. High-angle subduction to the NNE added further to the Coastal Batholith of Peru, but the plate motion was now almost parallel to the Colombian plate margin. This caused strike–slip displacement of a sliver of oceanic crust (the future Western Cordillera) along the Cauca–Patia Fault Zone, and arc activity there died out as subduction ceased. A further shift in plate motion direction at 40 Ma (Figure 6.3c), restored relatively high-angle convergence, and thus arc magmatism (episode D) to Colombia, with no respite in arc activity for the Coastal Batholith in Peru.

This model is not so cavalier with plate motions as it may seem at first. There is evidence for sudden shifts in plate motion from abrupt inflections in hot-spot traces (e.g. the bend in the Hawaii–Emperor seamount chain: DP and Block 1, Section 1.2). It is likely that any change in plate motion or configuration in one region will have a knock-on effect on other plates. Extrapolation to earlier times is tricky, but the basic point that plate motion and plate margin geometry conspire to affect the response of the crust is sound.

- Are there any other reasons why portions of oceanic crust would not be subducted at a convergent margin?

- Yes — oceanic crust that was particularly buoyant or thickened might resist subduction, and be partially obducted onto the continental margin instead.

Recent work on the lavas within the western Colombian terranes has drawn interesting parallels with rocks found on the Ontong–Java Plateau, a vast, thick, mostly submarine, **oceanic flood basalt** province mentioned briefly in Block 2, Section 5 and Figure 5.1. Geochemical similarities include flat chondrite-normalized REE patterns, a narrow range in MgO, and a lack of the Nb and Ta depletions that are characteristic of arc lavas. Unlike most fragments of ocean floor emplaced by **obduction** onto continental margins (ophiolites), there are very few vertical dykes in the Colombian Terranes; the basalts dominantly occur as flat-lying sills or flows. Exposures of deeper crustal (and mantle) rocks such as cumulate gabbros and peridotites imply a crustal thickness of 8–20 km, far thicker than ordinary oceanic crust. The presence of basic and ultrabasic lavas (picrites and komatiites) that are Mg-rich and have very high melting temperatures suggests that unusually hot mantle (and hence a mantle plume) was involved in their origin. These lines of evidence suggest that the Colombian exotic terranes originated as parts of an oceanic flood basalt plateau (Figure 6.4) generated in the SE Pacific region above a mantle plume. Remnants of this province are now dispersed throughout the Caribbean, and are believed by some researchers to be the earliest outpourings from the Galápagos plume (Block 2, Figure 5.1). Unlike the Ontong–Java Plateau, this plateau was accreted soon after its formation (< 25 million years), when it was still relatively warm, and thus very buoyant. The thick, buoyant crust resisted subduction, and accreted along transcurrent faults. Later thrusting exposed the deeper levels of the plateau at the surface. A model for the anatomy of this intraplate oceanic plateau, based largely on the terranes of western Colombia, is shown in Figure 6.4. The accretion of such volumes of anomalous oceanic material at convergent margins is clearly a powerful mechanism for extending the continents.

Question 6.2 Examine Figure 6.4 to answer the following questions about the anatomy of the accreted oceanic plateau in western Colombia. (a) Which two modes of igneous activity contribute to the formation of an oceanic plateau? (b) Summarize the main geological evidence given in Figure 6.4 for each of these two modes of igneous activity.

Question 6.3 It is very rare to observe the lower levels of an obducted oceanic plateau like some of these sections in western Colombia — usually only the uppermost levels, mostly lavas, are scraped off and accreted during obduction. Suggest a reason why so much of this particular plateau has been obducted onto the continental margin.

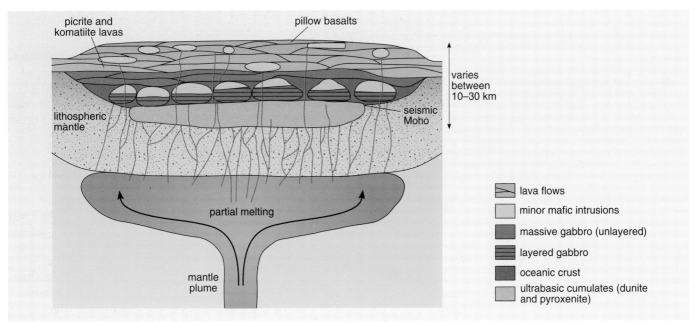

Figure 6.4   Schematic cross-section through an oceanic plateau based on accreted sequences in the Caribbean and Colombia. Not to scale.

In Colombia, terrane accretion has involved obduction of an oceanic plateau, whereas in other areas, such as NW America and SE Asia, destructive plate boundaries have grown by accretion of island arcs. The accretion mechanism can involve oblique or head-on collision (e.g. Figure 2.8), but despite the apparently diverse types of crust and mode of collision, there are two common factors.

● In what two ways does accreted crust differ from normal oceanic crust?

● The accreted crust is thicker and more buoyant (either because of a compositional difference or because it is hotter than old oceanic crust).

6.2   Accreted prism complexes

In Sections 2 and 5, we discussed models for the general anatomy of accretionary prisms, based on present-day prism systems. The following Section introduces a case study of a subduction complex that has been accreted to its corresponding continental arc margin on the west coast of North America. Because most present-day prisms are submarine, only indirect geophysical study is usually possible; the Franciscan Complex, by contrast, is exposed on land, allowing direct observation of the structures and metamorphic assemblages in different parts of the prism.

This Section is divided into two parts. The first describes the geology of central California, setting the accreted prism in context and exploring its structural and metamorphic characteristics. The second part focuses on structural aspects of the complex, using this evidence to develop ideas about prism mechanics, and to compare models for the accretion and exhumation history of the prism.

6.2.1   Geology of central California

As in western Colombia, California's mountain ranges and intervening basins trend parallel to the continental margin, striking NNW–SSE. California's geology can be split into four divisions, mapped out in Figure 6.5a. The first of these are the tracts of land dominated by Mesozoic (mainly Cretaceous) calc-alkaline plutons intruding deformed metamorphic basement that make up the Sierra Nevada and Klamath mountain ranges. Second is the Great Valley, a topographic low easily distinguished on the DP just east of San Francisco at 122 °W, 38 °N. This depression is underlain by at least 12 km of mainly undeformed late Jurassic to early Tertiary marine clastic sediments, implying it was an extensional basin during their deposition. The base of the sequence has depositional contacts — in places — on both the Sierra Nevada basement to the east, and ocean-floor rocks (the mid–late Jurassic Coast Range Ophiolite) to the west. However, many contacts are tectonic, including the Coast Range Fault Zone, the boundary between the ophiolite and the Franciscan Complex forming the coastal ranges of California. The Franciscan Complex is our third geological division and certainly lives up to the second part of its name: it is a complicated mixture of marine rock types (see Table 6.2) that are commonly jumbled together on a scale of a few metres in a mélange. The highly deformed marine sediments that dominate this zone have experienced different degrees of metamorphism, as you will see later in this Section. Fourth is the Salinian Block found in the extreme west of California, across the San Andreas Fault. It is a zone of almost identical geology to the Sierra Nevada magmatic zone. This terrane was probably displaced northwards along the fault from a region to the south corresponding to, or even continuous with, the Sierra Nevada.

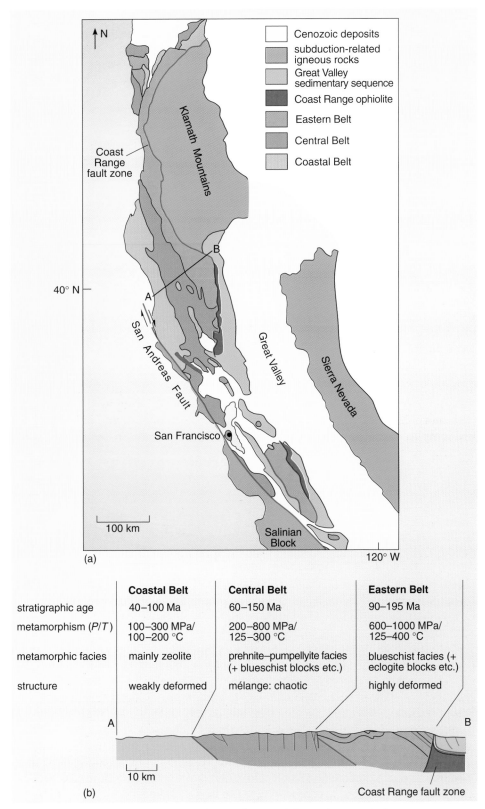

	Coastal Belt	**Central Belt**	**Eastern Belt**
stratigraphic age	40–100 Ma	60–150 Ma	90–195 Ma
metamorphism (P/T)	100–300 MPa/ 100–200 °C	200–800 MPa/ 125–300 °C	600–1000 MPa/ 125–400 °C
metamorphic facies	mainly zeolite	prehnite–pumpellyite facies (+ blueschist blocks etc.)	blueschist facies (+ eclogite blocks etc.)
structure	weakly deformed	mélange: chaotic	highly deformed

Figure 6.5 (a) Map of western California showing Mesozoic tectonic features, including the three belts that make up the Franciscan Complex (not labelled) and the San Andreas Fault. The line of the cross-section in (b) is marked A–B. (b) Cross-section highlighting the three subdivisions of the Franciscan Complex.

● Three of the major geological zones in California (Sierra Nevada, Great Valley and Franciscan Complex) correspond to the following three paleoenvironments: fore-arc basin, accretionary prism and magmatic arc. From the descriptions of their geology given above, decide which is which.

● The Sierra Nevada, dominated by calc-alkaline plutons, represents the Mesozoic magmatic arc. The Great Valley, with its great thickness of marine sediments, corresponds to the Jurassic–Tertiary fore-arc basin, filled with detritus from the Sierra Nevada. The Franciscan Complex was the late Mesozoic accretionary prism, which has been subsequently uplifted during accretion to the continental margin.

The variety of rock types in the Franciscan Complex is illustrated by Table 6.2, which summarizes the main sedimentary, igneous and metamorphic rocks found in this part of California. They are mostly Jurassic or Cretaceous in age (i.e., 206 to 144 Ma, and 144 to 65 Ma, respectively). Field photographs of some of these rock types are shown in Figure 6.6.

Table 6.2   Principal rock types of the Franciscan Complex. Much of the complex is made up of fairly coherent sections of marine sediment (clastic turbidites or chert), but there are significant bodies of mélange with shale or serpentinite matrix hosting blocks of all the other lithologies.

Rock type	Age	Origin
shale*	160–90 Ma	marine sediments: distal portions of turbiditic fans
greywacke, sandstone	160–90 Ma	marine sediments: proximal portions of turbiditic fans
chert	c. 195–90 Ma	marine sediments indicating slow accumulation of microscopic siliceous organisms in deep water
limestone	Cretaceous	marine sediments indicating slow accumulation of microscopic calcareous organisms in quite shallow water far from the continental landmass, possibly on seamounts
basalts (typically altered)	190–150 Ma	mafic ocean floor volcanics, including pillow lavas and pyroclastic deposits
serpentinite*, peridotite	Jurassic	mantle rocks, possibly from Coast Range ophiolite
amphibolite facies rocks	165–92[†] Ma	deformed and metamorphosed mafic rock
blueschist facies rocks	165–92[†] Ma	sediments and volcanics metamorphosed at moderate depths (20–35 km)
eclogite facies rocks	165–92[†] Ma	mafic rocks metamorphosed at great depths (> 40 km)

* Indicates rock types forming matrix of mélange; others are generally blocks or more coherent units.

† Indicates age of metamorphism.

Question 6.4   From the information in Figure 6.5 and Table 6.2, answer these questions on the Franciscan Complex. (a) What two rock types in the Franciscan Complex have the oldest stratigraphic age? (b) What depositional environment do the rocks in (a) represent? (c) What do the younger rock types in the accretionary complex tell us about how this depositional environment changed later in the Mesozoic?

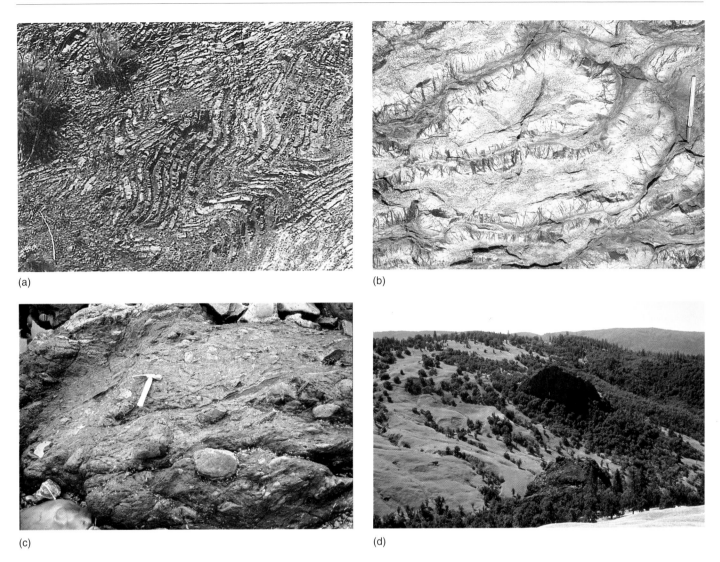

(a)

(b)

(c)

(d)

Figure 6.6   (a) Folded pelagic cherts, California. Cherts with these distinctive, regular, parallel-sided beds are known as 'Ribbon Cherts'. (b) Pillow basalts on Santa Catalina Island, southern California. The dark colour of the pillows' rims is due to growth of Na-rich amphibole, suggesting that these basalts were metamorphosed at significant depth during partial subduction (as explained later, in Box 6.1). (c) Typical mélange from the Coastal Ranges, California, with a variety of sedimentary, igneous and metamorphic blocks in a very weakly metamorphosed mud matrix. (d) Typical mélange scenery. Two large blocks (known locally as 'knockers') of metamorphosed basaltic rock standing proud of the softer matrix (grassy slopes).

From your answers to Question 6.4, you have painted a picture of an oceanic basin with deep-water pelagic cherts draping pillow basalts, gradually evolving into a basin near a continental landmass that filled up with considerable thicknesses of clastic sediment, brought down by turbidity currents from the continental shelf. This could record a simple cycle of oceanic crust generation at a spreading ridge, followed by pelagic sedimentation increasingly influenced by continental input as that portion of oceanic crust moved away from the ridge and eventually reached the North American margin.

There are further clues to the origin of some of the rocks in the Franciscan Complex: mid-Cretaceous limestones containing fossil foraminifera (planktonic organisms) that flourished in a tropical ocean, for example. Paleomagnetic data suggest that some of the limestones (e.g. Laytonville Limestone) were formed 17° S of the equator, while other rocks (e.g. Permanente Limestone, and pillow basalts near San Francisco), were originally formed north of the equator.

● What two deductions about terrane movement can you make from these paleomagnetic data on the rocks of the Franciscan Complex?

● First, the Laytonville Limestone has been displaced by a vast distance (as much as 5000 km) northwards to its present location (about 225 km N of San Francisco). Secondly, different rocks within the Franciscan Complex have travelled different distances — most of the complex probably originated closer to its current position than did the Laytonville Limestone.

The distances travelled by this terrane are on a similar scale to the motion of the Cache Creek terrane mentioned in Block 1.

One aspect of the Franciscan Complex you have not considered yet is the variety of metamorphic rocks occurring there, which are briefly referred to in Table 6.2. As we saw in Section 2.2, subduction zones generate a characteristic thermal anomaly in the lithosphere, which is colder than the surrounding regions. This gives rise to an equally distinctive metamorphic signature, with a higher P/T ratio than other tectonic settings, and the development of metamorphic mineral assemblages unique to these conditions. Box 6.1 describes this type of metamorphism in the context of metamorphic facies.

Box 6.1 Metamorphism of subduction zone rocks

You will probably already have met the concept of metamorphism — changes in rocks due mainly to changes in pressure and temperature. In studying metamorphic rocks, it is convenient to divide pressure–temperature (P–T) space up into named fields as a classification system. Figure 6.7 shows a scheme which uses the concept of **metamorphic facies**. Here, each field is defined by the distinctive assemblage of minerals that grow in the rocks for that range of conditions. This scheme is based on the minerals developed in mafic rocks such as basalt, which is fortunate for us as many of the metamorphic rocks in subduction zones are of a similar mafic composition.

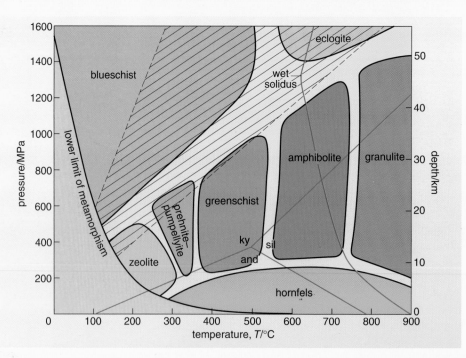

Figure 6.7 Diagram illustrating the division of P–T space into metamorphic facies. Also shown is the range of conditions commonly encountered in accretionary prisms and deeper levels of subduction zones (blue hatched area). The solidus of wet basalt and the stability fields of the aluminium silicate minerals (composition Al_2SiO_5) sillimanite (sil), kyanite (ky) and andalusite (and) are shown for reference.

Table 6.3 (opposite) lists the metamorphic facies typical of subduction zones and some of the distinctive minerals developed in rocks of different compositions. These compositions reflect the different components of the subduction zone setting.

Table 6.3 Metamorphic facies and characteristic minerals developed in a typical subduction zone.

Metamorphic facies	Mafic rocks (oceanic crust)	Pelitic rocks (accretionary prism sediments)	Typical setting
zeolite	zeolite minerals	*(few developed)*	ocean floor basalt; upper few km of prism
prehnite–pumpellyite	prehnite, pumpellyite	*(few developed)*	shallow levels of prism, low *T*
blueschist	lawsonite, epidote, blue amphibole	phengite, blue amphibole, kyanite	deeper levels in prism; downgoing oceanic slab
eclogite	garnet, pyroxene, blue amphibole	garnet, kyanite, rutile, phengite	deepest levels of subducting slab; not developed *in situ* in prism

Many of these names will be unfamiliar to you, but Activity 6.1 will introduce you to the most important minerals developed in blueschist and eclogite facies rocks (Figure 6.8). Most rocks will grow other minerals in addition to those given in Table 6.3 during high-pressure metamorphism; for instance, garnet is common in blueschist facies pelites. Conversely, not all rocks grow minerals in the zeolite or prehnite–pumpellyite facies on their journey down the subduction zone, particularly if fluid is not readily available. Wholesale recrystallization and new mineral growth may only occur in the blueschist and eclogite facies, in the deeper parts of the system.

Not all blueschist facies rocks are blue. The blue colour is imparted mainly by the blue sodic amphibole glaucophane, but this is absent from many pelitic blueschists, which are typically pale rocks due to the absence of biotite. Blueschist facies rocks are commonly altered to greenschist facies rocks, which are generally (though not invariably!) green, because many minerals (such as chlorite) formed at greenschist conditions have a green colour. Basaltic eclogite, a coarsely crystalline rock, has a very striking appearance due to the juxtaposition of the two essential minerals: red garnet and a bright green, sodic pyroxene named omphacite.

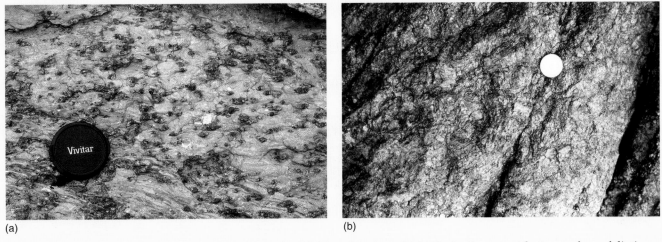

(a)   (b)

Figure 6.8   Typical high-pressure metamorphic rocks. (a) Blueschist from Ile de Groix, France, with strong planar foliation formed by glaucophane and white mica. Isolated red crystals are garnet, with rims of green chlorite. (b) Eclogite from Norway, with characteristic green groundmass of pyroxene studded with red garnets.

Activity 6.1   Metamorphic rocks from subduction zones

Now you should complete Activity 6.1 in *Workbook 3*. This Activity introduces you to typical (and very attractive!) examples of blueschist and eclogite facies rocks using the *Digital microscope* and other resources. You should take about 60 minutes to do this Activity.

Figure 6.5b shows that geologists commonly subdivide the Franciscan itself into three belts (Coastal, Central and Eastern), each of which may contain several, smaller terranes of different ages and origins. However, this division highlights some striking changes in character across the accreted prism that relate to the processes discussed earlier in the Block.

⬤ On a transect from west to east in the Franciscan in Figure 6.5b, what are the major changes?

⬤ Stratigraphic age: rock age generally increases eastwards; metamorphism: both temperature and pressure increase eastwards; deformation: general increase from west to east, though disrupted mélange is more prevalent in the Central Belt.

A final point to note is the age of metamorphism in the last three rows of Table 6.2. First, metamorphism characteristic of subduction occurred over a long period (70 million years) — and therefore subduction must have been just as long-lived. Secondly, the earliest metamorphism occurred only 25 Ma or so after the initial creation of the oceanic crust. In the next subsection, we will use these observations to unravel the evolution of this long-lived subduction complex, and test some current ideas on accretionary prism mechanics.

6.2.2 Prism mechanics and exhumation processes in California

Although the accretion of the Franciscan Complex to the continental margin has involved some deformation (mainly faulting), the accretionary prism has been preserved with many features intact. In the west, younger, less metamorphosed rocks represent the toe of the prism. In the east, the sediments are older and more metamorphosed, while blocks of other rock types in mélanges display even more extreme blueschist facies or eclogite facies metamorphism. This is typical of the rear portions of prisms (Figure 5.8), where rocks have been exhumed from depths of 30–60 km. It is unlikely that the exposure of rocks from such different depths is due to simple variation in erosion rates across the prism; we must appeal to some other process (or a combination of several!) to explain this extreme exhumation.

Before you address this puzzle, look at Figure 6.9, which illustrates a **pressure–temperature path** (P–T path) through time for a typical high-pressure Franciscan rock, compared to rock samples from other subduction complexes,

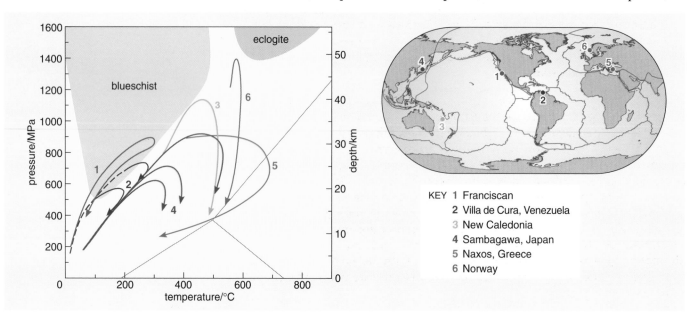

Figure 6.9   Pressure–temperature (P–T) paths for various subduction complexes (explained in the key). These paths are constructed using information on the stability of particular metamorphic minerals, as discussed in Block 4.

and a high-pressure complex formed during continental collision (Norway). Pressure is directly related to crustal depth, so paths of increasing pressure on this diagram represent burial of rocks. Temperature also increases with depth in the crust, as you saw in Block 1, but the rate of increase (the geothermal gradient) varies from place to place. Subduction zones are characterized by relatively cool geothermal gradients, which would plot as steep lines running from the origin through the blueschist facies field. Normal continental geotherms have a shallower slope. Paths 1 to 4 follow burial paths that are typical of subduction complexes, reflecting a cool geotherm. Once they have attained their peak pressure, however, those paths diverge markedly as the rocks return to lower pressures.

○ What process does the path of decreasing pressure represent for each rock?

○ If the pressure recorded by the rock is decreasing, the rock must be moving to shallower levels in the crust. This decompression portion of any *P–T* path therefore corresponds to the exhumation of the rock from depth back towards the surface.

Two paths (Villa de Cura and Franciscan) have a 'hairgrip' geometry, indicating that they cooled during exhumation (known as the 'Franciscan' type). Others (known as the 'Sambagawa' type) were exhumed without significant cooling, a more common scenario. This isothermal decompression generally indicates rapid exhumation, similar to that seen in continental collision environments (e.g. Norway). Some settings experience heating during decompression (e.g. Naxos), which endangers the preservation of the high-pressure assemblages.

You will notice that there is no absolute time information on these pressure–temperature paths, and you might be tempted to ask how long rocks in the Franciscan Complex took to cycle through the prism. Question 6.5 provides some data to help you estimate those time-scales.

Question 6.5 Convergence rates at the Franciscan margin in the late Cretaceous were *c.* 100 km Ma^{-1}. For an average prism geometry (surface slope of 3° and basal décollement dip of 5°), *c.* 7 km of convergence are required for 1 km of burial. (a) How long would it take to bury a rock accreted to this prism to a depth of 30 km? (b) Peak metamorphism at 30 km depth was dated to 118 Ma in a block of blueschist facies metavolcanics in the Franciscan. Blueschist facies detritus in a 60-Ma-old sediment constrains the time of exposure of this same blueschist facies material at the surface. Assuming a similar burial rate to that in part (a), how long has this blueschist facies rock been buried in the prism in total? Give your answer to the nearest million years.

Your answer to Question 6.5b is one estimate of the 'residence time' of rock in the accretionary prism, based on the assumption of simple underplating of material at a rate equivalent to subduction. It shows that high-pressure metamorphism would follow hard on the heels of accretion. This rapid burial is confirmed in some cases where fossils indicate the stratigraphic age of accreted sediments that have subsequently been underplated and metamorphosed. The range of metamorphic ages in the complex suggests protracted accretion, which is followed by slow cooling during exhumation towards the surface. The time-scales in Question 6.5 are typical of the eastern part of the Franciscan Complex; in fact, residence times vary from 30 to 70 Ma, and crude estimates of exhumation rates range from 0.3 to 0.9 km Ma^{-1}. With the evidence available, is it possible to choose between the different models for exhumation (Section 5.1.2) in this accretionary prism?

The corner flow and channel flow models may apply on a small scale to blocks of high-pressure rock in mélanges within the Franciscan, but not to the larger, more coherent sedimentary sections. Flow rates would be similar to convergence rates, implying exhumation of material in less than 1 Ma, and complete recycling of high-pressure rocks to the prism toe after about 2 Ma. The relative coherence of the toe region, and the wide range of ages across the prism, indicate that neither corner flow nor channel flow can apply to the whole prism. It may act on a local scale within the prism, for instance in the form of buoyant mud or serpentinite diapirs, which could bring entrained high-pressure blocks rapidly to the surface despite their high density. Looking again at Figure 6.9, you will notice that none of the subduction-related paths (1–5) pass through the eclogite field, and in fact even the thickest accretionary prisms would not reach eclogite facies conditions at their bases. However, eclogite facies rocks clearly occur within accretionary prisms exposed today, generally as exotic blocks in prism sediments metamorphosed at much shallower depths, as in the Franciscan Complex. The localized channel flow described in Section 5.1.2 may provide the solution to this puzzle, flushing eclogite facies rocks up from greater depths in the subduction zone until they are emplaced into the soft prism material.

The observation that rocks are being exhumed while convergence and accretion are ongoing is predicted by the dynamic wedge theory, as is the distribution of stratigraphic age and metamorphic grade of rocks along the upper surface of the prism. Direct evidence for the structures related to exhumation is more obscure, however. Some workers propose that the Coast Range Fault Zone acted as a low-angle extensional fault when the prism became overthickened, resulting in exhumation of rocks in its footwall, and the distinct metamorphic break across the fault suggests this may have occurred. In most accretionary complexes, many generations of complicated structures are overlain on each other, so that it is difficult to assess their relative importance. Each new episode of deformation modifies or erases earlier structural clues to the processes operating in the prism.

A final alternative solution to the exhumation problem, however, erases all evidence of the process as it operates! Erosion of the prism surface would eventually expose deep-seated rocks if it continued for a long period in conjunction with thrust faulting in the prism. This requires that the accretionary prism is above sea-level throughout, so that material is continuously scraped off the top. The detritus removed could disappear back down the subduction zone, leaving no clues to the erosion behind. However, as you saw earlier in this Block, sub-aerial accretionary prisms are quite rare (and sea-level is relatively low in the present era). It seems unlikely that erosion alone could account for much exhumation in this setting, though it may contribute in some cases. Most of the exhumation is probably due to the tectonic processes within prisms discussed throughout this subsection.

6.2.3 Paired metamorphic belts

The association of accretionary complexes with island arcs has led to the concept of **paired metamorphic belts**. This simply highlights the juxtaposition of two commonly linear regions of the same age with contrasting geothermal gradients and therefore metamorphic character. The arc is dominated by relatively high temperatures at low pressures, due to the ascent and emplacement of arc magmas through the crust, while the subduction complex typically develops high-pressure, low-temperature metamorphism (Figures 6.9, 6.10a). This is because cool oceanic material at the surface is subducted faster than it can heat up by conduction and radioactive decay. As a result, the isotherms in the Wadati–Benioff zone and prism become depressed (Figure 6.10a). The concept of paired metamorphic belts was developed in Japan, based on the Mesozoic

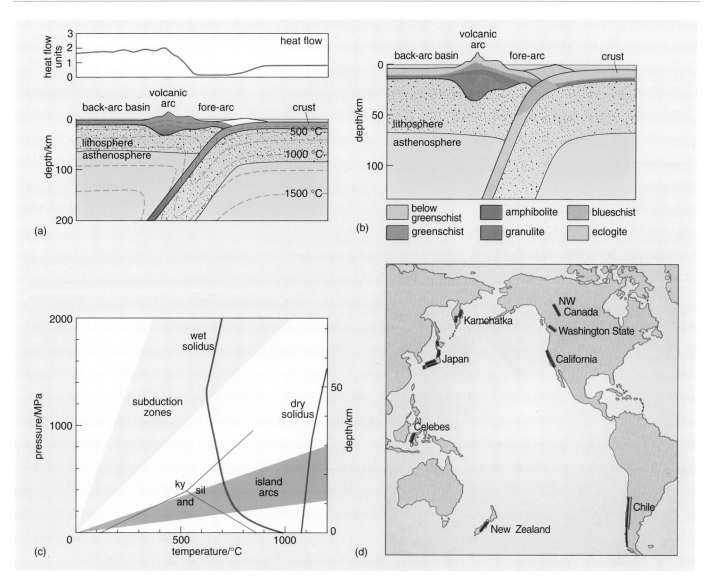

Figure 6.10 (a) Depression and elevation of isotherms in the trench and arc regions of a convergent margin, with surface heat flow across the same profile. (b) Cartoon based on the same section, with regions of different metamorphic facies highlighted. Note that there is a ×2 vertical exaggeration compared to (a). (c) Typical P–T conditions for subduction zone and arc-related metamorphism, relative to the stability fields of the aluminium silicates (Al_2SiO_5; ky = kyanite; sil = sillimanite; and = andalusite). The melting curves for wet and dry basalt are also shown. (d) Paired metamorphic belts around the Pacific margins.

Sambagawa (high-pressure) and Ryoke (low-pressure) belts. In California, the Franciscan Complex and Sierra Nevada batholith represent another paired belt, but several occur round the Pacific margins (Figure 6.10d).

Recognition of blueschist facies assemblages in older settings, particularly when paired with high-T, low-P belts, potentially allows us to identify ancient subduction zones. However, the further back into the geological record you search, the fewer blueschists you find: examples of this type of metamorphism are almost entirely confined to the Phanerozoic. This may be because such high-pressure mineral assemblages are rarely preserved; they will tend to be at least partially altered during exhumation unless they are kept relatively cool. Figure 6.9 shows that very few blueschists cool along a P–T path similar to their burial path; most either heat up during exhumation, or are brought towards the surface rapidly without much cooling. The older they are, the more chance there is of the high-pressure minerals being altered during subsequent changes in temperature and/or pressure, and the record of subduction lost. Another more radical theory suggests that during the Archean and Early Proterozoic, temperature increased more rapidly with depth than today, so that blueschists may not have been formed at all — indeed some geologists question whether subduction itself was possible. You will find further discussion of this controversy in Block 5.

6.3   Summary of Section 6

- Mountain ranges and basins running parallel to the coast in western Colombia reflect successive episodes of arc magmatism and transcurrent terrane accretion along strike–slip faults such as the Romeral Fault. This important lineament separates an ancient, essentially continental margin from younger oceanic terranes to the west.

- The docking ages of these terranes fall between the time their youngest crust formed, and the oldest age of plutons cutting the terrane boundary — or alternatively the oldest age of sedimentary material derived from across the terrane boundary after docking.

- Episodes of arc magmatism occurred during periods when convergence was at a relatively high angle (>25°), while terrane accretion was favoured during oblique convergence (<25°).

- Several lines of evidence, including narrow MgO range, flat chondrite-normalized REE patterns and an absence of Nb or Ta depletion, suggest the accreted terranes in western Colombia originated as oceanic plateaux rather than island arcs.

- California has an essentially tripartite geology, from east to west: the Sierra Nevada plutonic arc, the Great Valley fore-arc basin, and the Franciscan subduction complex. The latter includes fragments of ophiolitic ocean crust, deep marine sediments and trench sediments largely derived from the active margin.

- Within the Franciscan Complex, stratigraphic age, degree of deformation, and both metamorphic pressure and temperature, increase eastwards. This pattern matches the predictions of the dynamic wedge theory.

- Although the channel flow model may apply to restricted occurrences of mélange, particularly in the Central Belt of the Franciscan Complex, it cannot explain most features of the overall prism.

- Metamorphic rocks in the Franciscan Complex indicate that subduction was long-lived (70 Ma), and some high-pressure lithologies remained in the prism for as much as 60 Ma. Blueschist and eclogite facies rocks were exhumed from depths of 30 to 60 km.

- The characteristic association of paired high-pressure/low-temperature and high-temperature/low-pressure belts has been used as a marker for ancient subduction zones. Such belts are very rare in the Precambrian, which some researchers believe indicates that different tectonic conditions prevailed at that time.

Objectives for Section 6

Now that you have completed this Section, you should be able to:

6.1 Understand the meaning of all the terms printed in **bold**.

6.2 Describe the geology of western Colombia, and relate its various components to processes of transcurrent terrane accretion.

6.3 Understand how the timing of events involved in the assembly of the various terranes and plutons in western Colombia can be established.

6.4 Describe the basic anatomy and geochemical features of an oceanic plateau and discuss its relevance to Colombia and the Caribbean region.

6.5 Outline the geology of California, and place its main components in the context of subduction complex accretion.

6.6 Discuss in some detail the structural and metamorphic geology of the Franciscan Complex, including the time-scales of its evolution and conditions of formation.

6.7 Appreciate the nature of subduction zone metamorphism, including some typical rocks and minerals formed under high-pressure/low-temperature conditions.

6.8 Evaluate the applicability of contrasting models for accretionary prism mechanics in the light of evidence marshalled mainly from the Franciscan Complex.

6.9 Understand the concept of paired metamorphic belts.

7 Crustal growth and thickening at arc margins

Sections 5 and 6 examined the mechanisms by which existing crustal material is added to convergent margins. These processes of accretion or recycling involve no actual extraction of new crustal material from the mantle reservoir, and thus no net growth of continental crust on a global scale. The single most important mechanism of such net crustal growth today is subduction-related magmatism. This final Section reveals how mantle melts modify the arc crust at depth, and evaluates the contributions of different processes to crustal growth in the Andes.

There are two parts to Section 7. First, the petrology and geochemistry of plutonic arc rocks are introduced. This leads into a discussion of the Andean mountain chain, and a comparison of different parts of the Andes where contrasting processes have contributed to crustal thickening. Secondly, crustal growth rates at convergent margins are examined, both in the context of recent examples (Andes), and theories on crustal processes further back in time.

7.1 Plutonism in arcs and crustal growth

7.1.1 Plutonic rocks in arcs

The bodies of magma that feed volcanoes eventually solidify to form plutons, which will become exposed once uplift and erosion take their course. Since active volcanic arcs comprise a linear array of volcanic centres, their eroded remnants are represented by narrow strings of plutonic complexes. In a mature

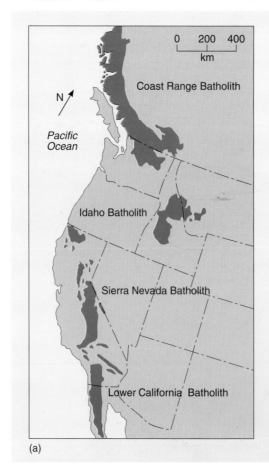
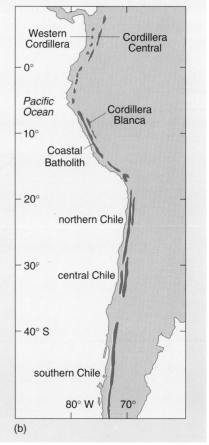

(a)   (b)

Figure 7.1   (a) The geology of western North America is dominated by four large batholiths (red) mostly emplaced during the Mesozoic (mid-Cretaceous) in response to the eastward subduction of Pacific ocean floor. (b) Mesozoic to Cenozoic batholiths (red) in South America.

arc that has been generating magma for tens of millions of years, the plutons will amalgamate at depth into a linear body known as a **batholith**, like those that characterize most of the western margin of the Americas (Figures 7.1, 7.2). The Andean batholith belt contains over 1000 plutons, the legacy of Mesozoic to Recent subduction at the Peru–Chile trench. The intrusive rocks that make up these plutons — gabbro, diorite and granite — crystallize from the same magmas as their volcanic equivalents basalt, andesite and rhyolite.

Figure 7.2   Part of the Sierra Nevada batholith makes up all of the exposure in this view of Yosemite National Park, California.

Mineralogy is a crucial element in the rigorous description of plutonic rocks, and hence it is their modal mineralogy that forms the basis of a classification scheme. Since plutonic rocks are generally medium- to coarse-grained, this scheme is easy to apply — even in the field, to a degree. Most plutonic rocks in arcs fall into the broad group known as **granitoids**, plutonic rocks containing different proportions of quartz, alkali feldspar and plagioclase (as well as other minerals). Figure 7.3 shows the internationally used ternary diagram subdividing granitoids by virtue of their relative proportions of these three minerals — it is known as the **QAP** (**q**uartz–**a**lkali feldspar–**p**lagioclase) diagram. Some rocks that may be familiar to you already (granite, diorite and gabbro) plot on this diagram, with granite distinguished clearly by the higher proportion of quartz and alkali feldspar. Diorite contains more of the

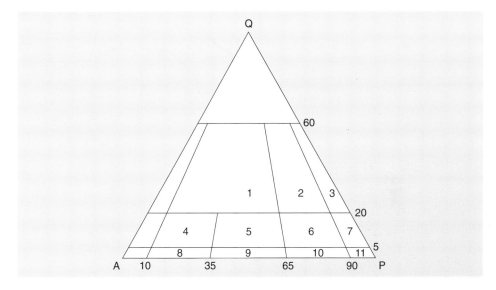

Figure 7.3   The modal Q (quartz) – A (alkali feldspar) – P (plagioclase) classification of granitoids. The numbered fields are as follows: 1 granite; 2 granodiorite; 3 tonalite; 4 quartz syenite; 5 quartz monzonite; 6 quartz monzodiorite; 7 quartz diorite; 8 syenite; 9 monzonite; 10 monzodiorite; 11 gabbro and diorite.

mafic minerals (e.g. biotite, hornblende or pyroxene) than granite; gabbro is mainly composed of plagioclase and pyroxene, typically some olivine, and only in rare cases small quantities of quartz and alkali feldspar that crystallized from the last traces of highly evolved interstitial liquid. Most gabbros would therefore plot on the P apex of the QAP diagram, and for these and other rocks with > 90% mafic minerals there are separate classification systems. A gabbro lacking either quartz or alkali feldspar (or both) would not, strictly speaking, be termed a granitoid, and most gabbros in fact fall outside the granitoid field. Since the bulk of plutonic rocks in arcs can be described using this scheme, we employ it throughout this Section.

> **Question 7.1** The QAP diagram is divided into fields on the basis of the proportions of quartz (horizontal lines) and the proportion of feldspar represented by plagioclase (steep lines). (a) Using Figure 7.3, state the critical distinction(s) between (i) granite and quartz monzonite; (ii) tonalite and granodiorite; (iii) tonalite and gabbro; (iv) quartz diorite and granodiorite. (b) Place the following in order of decreasing quartz/feldspar ratio: quartz monzodiorite, gabbro, granite.

In general, subduction zone plutonics fall into the fields numbered 1, 2, 3, 5, 6, 7 and 11 on Figure 7.3. Syenites and quartz syenites (fields 4 and 8) are rocks that are relatively rich in alkali feldspar and they crystallize from alkali-rich magmas, usually in within-plate settings; we will not consider them further here. Plutonic rocks in arcs, like their volcanic counterparts, display trends towards more evolved chemical compositions reflecting fractional crystallization and crustal assimilation processes (Section 4).

● Which of the common arc rock types — granite, diorite and gabbro — is the most evolved?

● Granite — its higher proportion of quartz and alkali feldspar reflects higher SiO_2 and K_2O contents. Gabbro and diorite represent the least-evolved rocks on the QAP diagram, plotting close to the P (plagioclase) corner.

Activity 7.1   Plutonic rocks from eroded arcs

Now attempt Activity 7.1 in *Workbook 3*. This introduces you to some typical examples of arc plutonic rocks using the *Digital microscope* and other resources. You should take about one hour to complete this Activity.

A further chemical classification from Block 2, using normative mineralogy, can be used to compare subduction zone plutonic rocks with those from other tectonic environments. One scheme discriminates on the basis of the relative proportions of alkalis, calcium and alumina in the rock. A rock containing abundant alumina will have normative corundum (C: Al_2O_3) appearing in the calculated norm; such rocks are termed peraluminous. If alkalis dominate, normative acmite (Ac: $NaFeSi_2O_6$) will appear in the norm calculation (acmite is a Fe^{3+} and sodium-bearing pyroxene, not covered in Block 2) and the rock is then defined as peralkaline. Intermediate between these two extremes are the metaluminous rocks, with normative anorthite (An: $CaAl_2Si_2O_8$) but *lacking* normative corundum. In fact, corundum is never observed in granites although it may occur in the calculated norm. This is because the norm calculation assumes that water is absent from the melt, whereas most granitic magmas contain 5–10% H_2O. This water favours the crystallization of hydrous minerals such as mica and amphibole rather than the anhydrous phases predicted by the norm calculation. The upshot is that modal mineralogy in granites has a much weaker correlation with the normative mineralogy than in basalts. The norms, however, do provide a useful basis for comparison of different plutonic magmas. Subduction magmas tend to be metaluminous, and as Table 7.1 shows, the other two divisions can also be broadly correlated with different tectonic settings. There are exceptions to this rough scheme: for instance, some highly evolved Andean granites are peraluminous, and there are rare occurrences of peraluminous granites in rift zones. The chemical differences arise from the differing P–T conditions and compositions of the magmas' source regions.

Table 7.1 Classification of igneous rock types by normative mineral, with their typical tectonic environments.

Tectonic setting	Characteristic normative mineral	Geochemical type
rift zone	acmite	peralkaline
subduction zone	anorthite (corundum absent)	metaluminous
continental collision zone	corundum	peraluminous

Compositional variation also occurs on the scale of single plutons. This commonly takes the form of a roughly concentric zonation, typically with less-evolved rock types (e.g. gabbro and diorite) exposed discontinuously around the pluton margins, while more-evolved rocks (granodiorite and granite) occupy the centre. This pattern is thought to arise from progressive solidification of a fractionating magma chamber, with the younger, more-evolved magmas intruding into the pluton core. Thus, in plutons we see the signature of the same processes we recognized in erupted magmas.

As well as this local variation, there are also compositional differences between plutons from separate arcs. These can be distinguished using the tholeiitic/calc-alkaline division introduced in Section 4, Figure 4.2. Figures 7.4 and 7.5 illustrate the mineralogical and chemical compositions of two plutons, the Finger Bay pluton in the Aleutian island arc and the Senal Blanca complex on the continental margin of Peru.

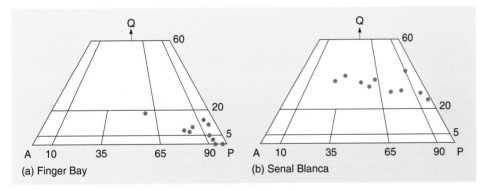

Figure 7.4 QAP diagrams for (a) the Finger Bay pluton (Aleutians) and (b) the Senal Blanca complex (Peru).

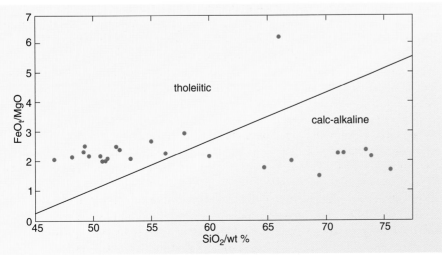

Figure 7.5 Plot of FeO_t/MgO against SiO_2 for rocks from the Finger Bay pluton (Aleutians) (purple) and the Senal Blanca complex (Peru) (red). The fields of tholeiitic and calc-alkaline magmas (from Figure 4.2) are shown.

Question 7.2 Compare and contrast the compositions of the island arc and continental margin plutons from Figures 7.4 and 7.5 in terms of (a) the range of SiO_2 contents; (b) their tholeiitic or calc-alkaline affinities; (c) the mineralogy and range of rock types.

The two plutons in Figures 7.4 and 7.5 are rather extreme examples of subduction zone rocks, and most other plutons exhibit a range of features intermediate between those of Finger Bay and Senal Blanca. However, these plutons tend to support the conclusions you drew from volcanic rocks about the differences between arc magmas on oceanic and continental crust. Oceanic island arcs tend to have mafic to intermediate tholeiitic magmas (gabbros, diorites and quartz monzonites). Continental margin arc magmas are generally intermediate to silicic and calc-alkaline. They typically include granodiorite and granite, with relatively high quartz/feldspar ratios.

● Which process(es) described in Section 4 are most likely to be implicated in these differences between oceanic and continental arcs?

● The more evolved continental magmas probably reflect assimilation of greater volumes of continental crust during their generation and ascent. A glance at Figure 2.9 shows that magmas in continental arcs ascend through a much greater thickness of crust, with more potential for assimilation of crustal material on the way than in oceanic arcs.

p 18.

There is supporting evidence from elevated $^{87}Sr/^{86}Sr$ ratios for varying degrees of assimilation between arcs. Studies in the Andes have even interpreted subtle differences in the $^{87}Sr/^{86}Sr$ ratio of igneous rocks as reflecting the different ages of continental basement through which the magmas ascended. Another general distinction between oceanic and continental arcs at depth is suggested by Figure 7.1. Continental margin plutons often reach considerable size (10 km across), and large numbers of them coalesce to form immense, continuous batholiths parallel to the plate margin. In contrast, island arc plutons tend to be both smaller and less numerous, forming a scattered chain of plutons.

With these basic components of plutonic belts in place, we can look in more detail at how they influence the processes of crustal growth at subduction zone margins.

7.1.2 Subduction and the geology of the Andes

The Andes stretch 8000 km along the continental margin of South America, a mountain range reflecting a long history of Mesozoic subduction, related magmatism and crustal thickening. The mere fact that the archetypal subduction zone lava, andesite, derives its name from these mountains might suggest that they represent a standard continental destructive plate margin. This initial impression is misleading, however, as a brief study of Figure 7.6 demonstrates.

Question 7.3 Examine Figure 7.6a–d, and describe how the following parameters vary along the Andean margin: (a) the distribution of active volcanoes; (b) the dip of the Wadati–Benioff zone; (c) the age and topography of ocean lithosphere entering the Peru–Chile trench; (d) the thickness of South American crust; (e) the main topographical features of the Andes.

Clearly there are variations in features of both the subducting and overriding plates along the Andean margin that may be linked by the subduction process. One such link is the correlation of abundant silicic magmatism in the CVZ (Central Volcanic Zone as defined in the answer to Question 7.3) with thick crust that includes Precambrian basement (predominately silica-rich gneisses).

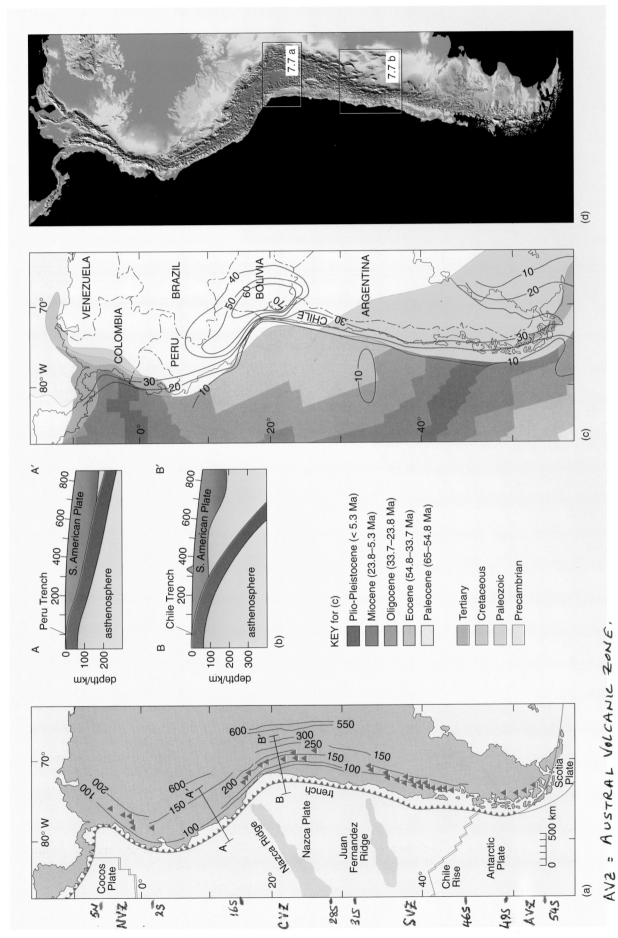

AVZ = AUSTRAL VOLCANIC ZONE.

Figure 7.6 (a) Map of the South American Plate margin showing locations of active volcanoes (triangles), and contours of depth to the Wadati–Benioff zone in km. A–A′ and B–B′ are the lines of section shown in (b). (b) Cross-sectional geometries of the Nazca and South American Plates inferred from seismicity in central Peru and northern Chile. Horizontal distances are measured from the trench in km. (c) Map showing the ages of the South American basement and ages of the adjacent sea-floor. Also shown are contours of crustal thickness in km. (d) Digital elevation model image of the Andes.

Although silicic magmatism could simply reflect fractional crystallization, the volumes generated in the CVZ indicate that crustal assimilation must also be involved, and elevated $^{87}Sr/^{86}Sr$ ratios confirm the contribution of ancient crust (Section 4.4). The thick Andean crust impedes the magmas' ascent, giving more opportunity for crustal assimilation and hence increased production of silicic magmatism. More fundamental are the gaps in volcanic activity along the plate boundary, which seem to coincide with flat-slab zones.

● Why is the dip of the subducting slab so gentle in these regions?

● Parts of the flat-slab regions are occupied by the aseismic Nazca and Juan Fernandez Ridges. Because these are particularly buoyant sections of lithosphere, they will not subduct as steeply into the mantle as normal oceanic lithosphere. Instead they sink beneath the South American margin at a low angle. This may also be true of the Chile Rise spreading ridge.

There is still debate over why shallow subduction should suppress volcanic activity in the overriding plate. One theory is that because the subducted slab dips at such a shallow angle beneath the continental lithosphere, the usual sub-arc mantle wedge is absent, and thus no melt can be generated. Why would the wet basaltic slab not melt instead? A number of answers to this question have been put forward, but the simplest is that in most cases the slab is too cold to melt. There are only a few localities where the arc magmas have a distinct geochemical signature that implies a contribution from partial melting of the hydrated slab. These magmas, known as **adakites**, are enriched in sodium, reflecting the alteration of the sea-floor basalts by seawater (Box 7.1).

Box 7.1 Adakites

Adakites (named after Adak Island in the Aleutians where these rocks were first recognized) are volcanic and intrusive subduction-related rocks with particular chemical characteristics. They have >56% SiO_2, > 3.5% Na_2O, and relative to 'normal' island arc volcanics they have low Y and HREE contents and high Sr contents. These compositional traits can be explained by partial melting of wet subducted basalt (eclogite) such that residual garnet, which has high K_d values for Y and HREE (e.g. Figure 4.17), produces partial melts that are impoverished in these trace elements. Interestingly, arc magmas with less than about 20 ppm Y (adakites) are found in arcs where the subducted lithosphere is less than 25 Ma old. Examples include parts of Central America, the Aleutians and Chile. 'Normal' arc magmas, with higher Y contents, are found where the subducted lithosphere is older. Thermal models of subduction indicate that oceanic crust younger than 25 Ma will still be warm enough for it to undergo partial melting after subduction, whereas older, colder lithosphere cannot melt. In this case, dehydration reactions in the slab lead to hydration of the mantle wedge which then undergoes partial melting to provide the parent magmas in arcs, as described in Section 3.

7.1.3 Crustal growth in the Andes

It has been estimated that granitoid rocks occupy 15% of the surface area of the Andes, translating to a volume of around 2 million cubic kilometres. The ages of these linear batholiths indicate that plutonic activity has moved eastwards with time, reflecting similar subduction-related processes along the length of South America apart from Colombia and Ecuador, where terrane accretion occurred (Section 6.1.2). The following summary of Andean evolution since the Permian illustrates some of the processes of crustal growth in the region.

The Permo-Triassic was a phase of extensional, mostly back-arc, basin formation in the Andean region, with basic igneous rocks intruding parallel to the continental margin. Subduction complexes formed along the southernmost part of the margin. Silicic arc volcanism began to dominate in the Jurassic, but it was not until the mid-Cretaceous that a shift in tectonic configuration sent the region into compression.

In extensional regimes, magmas can rise easily to the surface and erupt, using faults as natural conduits. With compression, this avenue of escape was closed off, leading to gabbroic intrusions at depth (magmatic underplating). The mafic crust around these intrusions melted, which along with fractional crystallization of the gabbros formed suites of granitoid magmas. These low-density granitoid magmas were channelled up deep, pre-existing fault zones, thereby both lowering the average crustal density and thickening the crustal section. With uplift and erosion, the plutons were exposed to show the characteristic zonation of older, more basic rims and younger, more evolved cores.

⬤ What was the source of the basic magmas that underpins this process of crustal growth?

⬤ As in most volcanic arcs, these primitive basic magmas were produced by partial melting of the enriched, hydrated mantle wedge (Section 3), modified in the more evolved rocks by fractional crystallization and crustal contamination (Section 4). This sequence of events gives rise to the typical calc-alkaline series of plutonic and volcanic rocks in the Andes.

However, the Cordillera Blanca in Peru (Figure 7.1b) contains atypical Na-rich plutonic rocks (equivalent to adakites) with relatively low $^{87}Sr/^{86}Sr$ ratios, whose geochemical characteristics suggest melting at about 50 km depth. These rocks may represent magmas derived from partial melting of either a subducted spreading ridge, or underplated basaltic material — perhaps the signature of an earlier episode of 'flat-slab' subduction.

Finally in this Section, a note of caution. The Andean topography (Figures 7.6d, 7.7) owes much to processes other than batholith growth and crustal addition. For instance, studies of fossil flora and fauna indicate that 20 million years ago the Altiplano plateau in the central Andes was only one-third of its present height above sea-level. The increase in elevation in this region is due mainly to crustal shortening

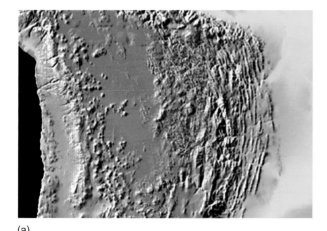

(a)

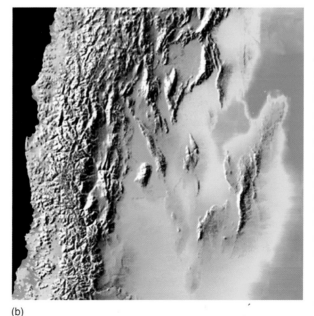

(b)

Figure 7.7 (a) Digital elevation model of the central Andes. The active arc (Western Cordillera) lies among the grey peaks just east of the coastal plain. The Altiplano plateau is the flat red region to the east of the arc. The sub-Andean fold and thrust belt shows up as a series of parallel ridges on the extreme eastern edge of the mountain range. (b) Digital elevation model of central Chile and Argentina. The Sierras Pampeanas basement uplifts show up clearly as distinct, linear, elevated blocks isolated from the main Andes.

— in fact, 80 to 90% of the excess crustal thickness under the Altiplano can be attributed to this deformation. The sub-Andean fold and thrust belt and the Sierras Pampeanas basement uplifts that you identified in Question 7.3 are both surface expressions of the compressional deformation that has contributed to this thickening.

⬤ If the majority of the recent crustal deformation in South America has occurred within the Andes, what does that imply about the crust in that region compared to the rest of the continent?

⬤ It implies the crust is weaker there than elsewhere in South America.

Why is this so? Well, first it is a question of heat flow. As you saw in Sections 2.2 and 6.2, volcanic arc crust (and also lithosphere) is hotter than adjacent regions. You may remember from Block 1 that young, hot lithosphere is weaker than old, cold lithosphere, and the same relationship holds in this case. Because the Andean lithosphere as a whole is under compression, it deforms by thickening. However, there is another factor influencing the relative strength of the crust in a mature arc like the Andes, and that is its composition.

⬤ How does the overall composition of a continental arc change as it matures?

⬤ There is a gradual trend towards more evolved magmas, with the emplacement of large batholiths of granite, granodiorite and tonalite. Thus, mature arcs are more siliceous than immature or oceanic arcs, which remain dominated by mafic rocks.

Mature arcs are similar in composition to typical continental crust, with a high proportion of quartz and feldspar. These minerals are weaker than the mafic minerals found in immature arcs (e.g. pyroxene, olivine, plagioclase), and quartz-bearing rocks in particular deform in a ductile fashion at quite low temperatures (250–300 °C). The implication is that the more evolved a volcanic arc becomes, the more susceptible it will be to deformation — even if the same thermal regime prevails.

Many arcs are in an extensional stress regime, rather than the compressional state of the Andes, which means they should be even more susceptible to deformation (Block 1, Section 3). Although oceanic lithosphere is stronger than continental lithosphere, it is in the oceanic realm that the best geological evidence for extension in arcs is found. In fact, one particular feature you have studied earlier in this Block is strongly linked with significant extension in arcs.

⬤ What feature is thought to result from extension acting on the weak crust in an oceanic volcanic arc?

⬤ An oceanic back-arc basin — and its associated remnant arc — such as the Mariana Trough and the West Mariana Ridge in the western Pacific. Geological evidence strongly suggests that the Mariana Trough represents a rift formed when a volcanic arc split straight down the middle.

The Aves Ridge and Grenada Basin in the Caribbean also seem to have resulted from the rifting of a weak arc in this way, and the abundance of remnant arcs implies this may be a relatively common process, despite the greater strength of oceanic lithosphere. Since these arcs are not nearly as evolved as the Andes, the thermal regime must exert a huge influence on lithospheric strength in the oceanic realm.

Not all of the Andean range is dominated by deformation, however. Crustal shortening accounts for as little as 30% of the crustal thickness in the CVZ, and magmatic addition in parts of the range contributes up to 40%. There is no doubt that, while pluton formation has provided a solid foundation for the Andes, compressional deformation is the main force behind the evolution of a fully fledged orogenic belt with thickened crust, and high plateaux such as the Altiplano or Tibet. The processes that form collisional mountain belts and these extraordinary plateaux are explored in Block 4 *Mountain Building.*

7.2 Rates of crustal growth at subduction zones

In this Section so far, you have explored how new crustal material is generated, ultimately, from the mantle and added to the arc crust — often becoming somewhat modified along the way. Can we estimate how rapidly this addition is occurring today? Is it possible to deduce whether the present growth rate is slower or faster than it was in the past?

7.2.1 Recent crustal growth rates

In order to measure how much the crust grows at the expense of the mantle, it is considerably easier to calculate the volume of material added to the crust than the volume extracted from the mantle. The batholiths of South America provide a good starting point for this exercise.

> Question 7.4 The Coastal Batholith of Peru is 1600 km long and 65 km wide, and was intruded at shallow depths (3–8 km) between 100 and 30 Ma ago. It has an estimated volume of 1×10^6 km^3. (a) Calculate the average crustal growth rate for this part of South America based on these figures. (b) Using your answer to part (a), calculate the growth rate of the Peruvian Coastal Batholith in terms of the rate of volume addition per kilometre of batholith length.

How useful are the answers to Question 7.4? Well, first they are based on an *estimate* of intruded magma volume, which is very difficult to assess accurately. Secondly, as you discovered in Section 4, some magmas have been formed or supplemented by melting and digestion of pre-existing crustal rocks, which would lead us to *overestimate* the volume of new material actually added to the crust. Thirdly, on the other hand, there are two unknown quantities that are likely to result in an *underestimate* of the added volume. One is the volume of buried material, for instance the batholith roots, which include large mafic intrusions in the lower crust (the gabbroic intrusions mentioned in Section 7.1.3). The second is the volume of material that has been removed by erosion, including the batholith roof zones and associated volcanic rocks erupted at the surface. Although we cannot easily account for the eroded material, we can turn to geophysical methods for a more accurate cross-section of the whole crust.

● How does the geophysical image of arc crust differ from that of 'normal' crust?

● Section 2.2 demonstrated that arc crust is thicker than in adjacent non-arc regions, and that the mid to lower arc crust in particular is thickened. A deep keel forms under the arc edifice.

You can see this keel clearly in the cross-section through the central Andes given in Figure 7.8. Taking the cross-sectional area of the keel and multiplying by the entire length of the arc gives the volume that the keel contributes to the overall volume of Andean crust. At this point, some allowance must be made for the fact that, as shown in Figure 7.6c, the size of this keel varies along the length of the mountain belt. This keel volume can then be included with the earlier estimate for the plutons and surface volcanic rocks to obtain the added crustal volume. Dividing this much larger volume by the age of subduction-related magmatism gives a much higher value for the crustal growth rate than that calculated for the Peruvian Batholith alone.

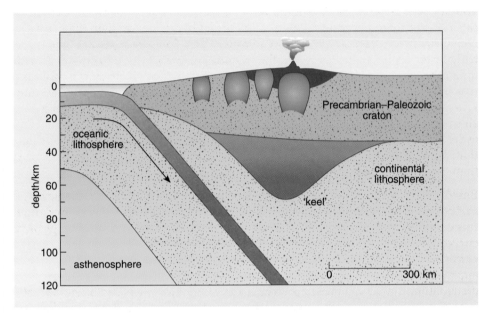

Figure 7.8 Schematic E–W cross-section through the South American Plate margin in the central Andes.

● Can you suggest why this value might represent an overestimate of material added to the crust in this region?

● Section 7.1.3 stated that up to 90% of the present crustal thickness in the central Andes is due to crustal shortening and thickening by deformation (folding and faulting) of pre-existing crust. So although the keel may be partly composed of igneous intrusions such as the mafic bodies in the lower crust, it is partly a result of deformation.

Taking this into account, for every kilometre of arc in the central Andes, it is estimated that about 30 km³ must be added to the crust every million years ($30 \, \mathrm{km^3 \, Ma^{-1} \, km^{-1}}$) in order to account for the cross-section in Figure 7.8. Estimates of growth rates by similar methods at other active continental margins and island arcs were broadly consistent with this figure until relatively recently. In the late 1990s, however, studies of the Aleutian and Izu–Bonin oceanic arcs independently arrived at much higher figures for crustal growth at those localities, on the order of $60 \, \mathrm{km^3 \, Ma^{-1} \, km^{-1}}$.

> **Question 7.5** The total length of active magmatic arcs on the Earth today is approximately 37 000 km. What is the current global rate of crustal growth at subduction zones, assuming the following average crustal growth rates? Express your answer in units of $\mathrm{km^3 \, Ma^{-1}}$. (a) $30 \, \mathrm{km^3 \, Ma^{-1} \, km^{-1}}$; (b) $60 \, \mathrm{km^3 \, Ma^{-1} \, km^{-1}}$.

In the following subsection, the estimates of the current crustal growth rate due to subduction that you calculated in Question 7.5 are compared with estimates of crustal growth rates further back in Earth's history.

7.2.2 Crustal growth rates in the past

Because we know the present volume of continental crust relatively well, it is a simple matter to divide this by the age of the Earth and obtain an average, long-term crustal growth rate. We can then compare that with our estimated crustal growth rates from Question 7.5.

> **Question 7.6** The volume of the continental crust is $7.8 \times 10^9\,\mathrm{km}^3$, and the age of the Earth is 4.55×10^9 years. Calculate the long-term growth rate of continental crust.

Your answer to Question 7.6 should tell you that the long-term crustal growth rate is faster than one of our growth rate estimates, but slower than the more recent estimate based on the two oceanic arcs. If the long-term growth rate is truly faster, then either there is another significant contribution to crustal growth today that has been overlooked (this is considered unlikely!), or crustal growth was indeed faster in the past. In fact, if the estimated growth rate from Question 7.5a ($1.1 \times 10^6\,\mathrm{km}^3\,\mathrm{Ma}^{-1}$) had operated throughout Earth history, we'd still be short of one-third of the continental crust! By contrast, if the more recent estimate is correct, it implies that crustal growth was slower in the past — either that, or these two oceanic arcs are atypical, and have a much higher growth rate than the rest at present.

Bearing in mind these uncertainties, it is no wonder that there is no consensus on how the continental growth rate has varied over time! Figure 7.9 shows just a few of the main variations proposed; you should bear in mind that these growth curves were generated by a range of different methods. While some use volumetric arguments similar to those developed in this Section, other approaches employ geochemical data (isotopic evolution, radiometric age distribution, clastic sediment geochemistry), and others are based on models of heat dissipation over Earth's history. Some workers (curves 1–3) believe the continents grew very quickly at an early stage, and have either been in steady state with destruction of crust balancing formation, or slowly increasing or decreasing since then. A less extreme view proposes a pulse of rapid growth at some stage in the Earth's history (curve 4), a popular time being around 2.5 to 3 Ga. Some researchers (curve 5) maintain that the long-term average growth rate has been constant, but with episodic bursts of growth. The final scenario is of an increased rate of growth in more recent times (Neoproterozoic to

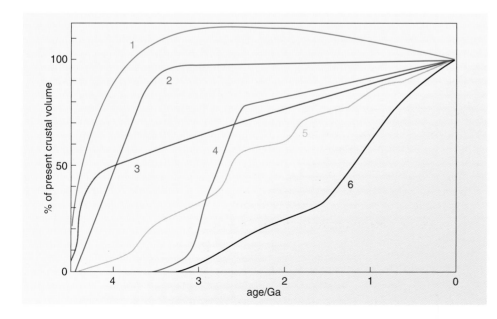

Figure 7.9 Set of curves illustrating different models for the growth of continental crust over Earth's history. The growth is shown relative to the current volume of continental crust at 100%. The numbered curves are explained in the text.

Phanerozoic — curve 6). This last view is currently out of fashion because it is thought that Archean tectonics differed from that of today in a way that favoured rapid crustal growth. One expression of this is that evidence for subduction-driven tectonics (blueschist-facies metamorphism, paired metamorphic belts, andesitic volcanism, ophiolites) is lacking prior to ~2 Ga.

The processes you have been learning about in this Block have therefore been major contributors to continental growth for at least the second half of the Earth's history. The tectonics and crustal evolution processes that may have dominated the earlier part of Earth's history is a topic that you will meet in Block 5.

7.3   Summary of Section 7

- Plutonic rocks containing modal quartz, plagioclase and alkali feldspar are known as granitoids. They are classified on the basis of the relative proportions of quartz, alkali feldspar and plagioclase, illustrated on the QAP triangular diagram.

- Granitoids in arc settings are typically metaluminous (normative anorthite but *no* normative corundum), in contrast to those from continental rifts (commonly peralkaline: normative acmite) and continental collision zones (commonly peraluminous: normative corundum).

- The roots of arc volcanoes, exposed in eroded arcs such as the Andes, form plutonic belts and batholiths running parallel to the ancient convergent plate margin.

- Arcs founded on continental crust generally develop calc-alkaline plutons, including the more silicic granitoids such as granite and granodiorite. Tholeiitic granitoids, and less evolved rock types (gabbros, diorites, quartz diorites and quartz monzodiorites) are characteristic of eroded oceanic island arcs.

- Individual plutons are commonly zoned, becoming more silicic towards their centres. In any one arc, there is also a general progression towards more evolved plutonic rock compositions with time.

- South of Ecuador in the Andes, huge calc-alkaline batholiths (e.g. the Coastal Batholith of Peru) have been emplaced since mid-Jurassic time into previously extended crust. This magmatic activity accounts for a significant amount of crustal *growth* in the Andes, though crustal *thickening* occurs partly by compressional deformation in the central Andes.

- Distinct gaps in the active magmatic arc correlate with regions where the downgoing oceanic plate subducts at a shallow angle. Although mantle melting is inhibited by this process, in rare cases there is evidence that the underplated basaltic material may melt instead to produce sodium-rich magmas.

- Estimates of the rate of crustal addition at arcs are obtained by dividing geophysically determined excess crustal volume by the duration of subduction. The average growth rate determined in this way is $30 \, km^3 \, Ma^{-1}$ per km of arc. For the entire globe, this rate is equal to a total growth rate of $1.1 \, km^3 \, yr^{-1}$. The most recent estimates of crustal growth in two oceanic arcs, however, is $60 \, km^3 \, Ma^{-1}$ per km.

- Subduction is responsible for the most important crustal growth mechanism currently operating. Whether continental growth was more rapid at some stage in the geological past, as is widely accepted, or involved mechanisms other than subduction-related magmatism, are topics of debate. The debate focuses on the accuracy of estimates of the current crustal growth rate and the geological evidence for subduction and other crustal growth processes in ancient rocks. The characteristic association of paired high-pressure/low-temperature and high-temperature/low-pressure metamorphic belts has been used as a marker for ancient subduction zones. Such belts are very rare in the Precambrian, which some believe indicates that different tectonic conditions prevailed at that time.

Objectives for Section 7

Now that you have completed this Section, you should be able to:

7.1 Understand the meaning of all the terms printed in **bold**.

7.2 Use the QAP classification scheme for plutonic igneous rocks, and be familiar with the mineralogy on which it is based.

7.3 Describe some of the variation in plutonic rocks in arcs, and between different arcs, in the context of modal and normative mineralogy, and basic geochemical characteristics.

7.4 Describe the various geological and geophysical characteristics of the Andean margin, including along-arc variations in subduction mode, crustal thickness and volcanism.

7.5 Account for the formation of the Andes in terms of magmatic and deformational processes, and outline the evolution of the mountain belt through time.

7.6 Demonstrate how estimates of the volumes and rates of magma generation at destructive margins can be extrapolated to give estimates of the current rates of global crustal growth.

7.7 Appreciate what implications these rates of current crustal growth have for crustal growth in the past, and whether plate tectonics has always operated as it does today.

Answers and comments to Questions

Question 2.1 (a) The Mariana arc has a very steep subduction angle, and should therefore be almost a straight line. However, it is quite strongly curved, which contravenes the geometric rule.

(b) The Lesser Antilles arc is moderately arcuate where the dip of the Wadati–Benioff zone is also moderate (45°). So here, it obeys the simple geometric rule. [*Note:* The arc becomes sharply curved towards its southern extreme, but here the Benioff zone steepens until it is almost vertical. This anomalous behaviour is caused by distortion of the subduction zone at its junction with the E–W strike–slip plate boundary with S. America.]

(c) The Tonga–Kermadec arc is nearly straight for most of its length, but the subduction zone dips at around 45° below the arc. For this moderate dip, the arc should be fairly arcuate — so Tonga disobeys the rule.

(d) The Kurile arc is moderately arcuate and its Wadati–Benioff zone dips at moderate angles (35° to 50°) so, like the central Lesser Antilles it obeys the rule quite well. (*Note:* in the Kurile arc, the Pacific slab there initially dips at around 35°, steepening to about 50° at 200 km depth.)

(e) Although subduction is at a very shallow angle in northern Chile, this segment of the arc is hardly curved at all. This may be because the slab has been torn into segments with different dips along this margin, as you will see in Section 7.1.2, so that the shallow segments are 'pinned' at either end and cannot develop an arcuate form. This example disobeys the rule.

Question 2.2 (a) In the (understandable!) absence of direct observation, geophysical methods must be used. In this case, scientists can combine two types of data: the distribution of earthquakes associated with the downgoing slab (Wadati–Benioff zone); and seismic refraction data, which map out the zone of high seismic velocity corresponding to the slab.

(b) First-motion studies (Block 1, Section 1.4) of earthquakes associated with the slab tell us whether any particular seismic event resulted from extension or compression. In most cases, compression or extension within the slab is parallel to the slab dip, as expected, but there are some examples of slab segments that show oblique first motions.

Question 2.3 Sketches of the three situations are given in Figure A2.1. Note that in the fore-arc–fore-arc collision (f), either oceanic plate could subduct beneath the collided arc following collision. In the continent–continent collision (e), subduction ceases entirely, whereas in (g), the oceanic plate on the far right will accommodate all the subduction once the back-arc ocean has been completely consumed.

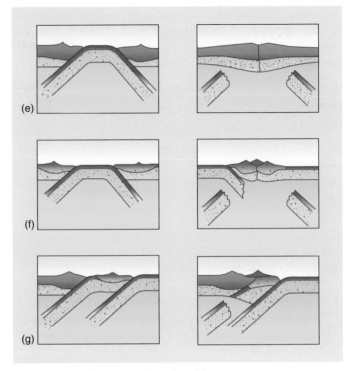

(e)

(f)

(g)

Figure A2.1 Answer to Question 2.3.

Question 2.4 (a) The upper crustal layer ($S_P = 0$ to 6.0 km s^{-1}) is thicker (6 to 8 km) in island arcs than in typical oceanic crust (about 2 km). Island arcs also have a thicker lower crustal layer ($S_P = 6.4$ to 7.2 km s^{-1}) than oceanic interiors (6 to 15 km compared to ~ 4 km respectively).

(b) Three layers are defined in terms of P-wave speeds within continental crust; these layers are also present in all the examples shown of active continental margins. The uppermost layer is about 10 km in the continental interior, similar to most active margins. In contrast, the 6.4 to 7.2 km s^{-1} layer is thicker at most active margins (10 to 45 km) than in the continental interior (*c.* 18 km). The middle crustal layer ($S_P = 6.0$ to 6.4 km s^{-1}) has variable thickness in active margins, ranging from only 5 km to 21 km (2.5 times as thick as in the continental interior). A dense transitional layer at the base of the crust occurs in the Colombian margin but is absent from Colorado; such transitions are, however, very variable features.

(c) Active continental margins generally have thicker crust than oceanic island arcs. In addition, whereas most island arcs possess two crustal layers, active continental margins have three. While the upper layers in oceanic arcs are only slightly thinner (6 to 10 km) than in continental margins, the lower layer (6.4 to 7.2 km s^{-1}) is usually thicker in active continental margins. One exception is in the Aleutians, where the oceanic arc has a thicker mafic lower crust than the Alaskan margin, but note that the Alaskan arc contains a layer of intermediate composition ($S_P = 6.0$ to 6.4 km s^{-1}), which marks it out as a continental arc. The Izu–Bonin oceanic arc is anomalous in this respect, and in addition has a dense transitional layer at the base of the arc crust.

(d) The uppermost portions of most mantle wedges beneath arcs have slightly lower S_P than the mantle beneath oceanic and continental interiors.

(e) The presence of a liquid reduces S_P, and the lower values of mantle S_P underneath volcanic arcs are attributed to small amounts of partial melt in the mantle wedge.

Question 2.5 (a) This negative anomaly reflects both the downward component of the slab–pull force on the subducting plate, and the large volume of low-density water (and/or sediment) that fills the trench itself.

(b) Under the fore-arc, there is a doubling-up of dense oceanic crust (fore-arc crust and underlying subducting slab) not far below the surface. This mass excess results in a positive anomaly over the fore-arc region.

(c) This minor positive anomaly mirrors the slight swell oceanward of the trench where the thin oceanic plate flexes upward just before plunging into the subduction zone. This flexure is the result of an upward force acting on the elastic plate.

Question 2.6 (a) The older the plate being subducted, the colder and denser the lithosphere entering the Wadati–Benioff zone is. This results in more marked depression of the isotherms in the subduction zone (as in NE Japan), a colder Wadati–Benioff zone, steeper subduction angle and thus a thicker mantle wedge. Young subducting lithosphere produces a relatively warm subduction zone, shallower subduction, and a thinner mantle wedge.

(b) Faster subduction increases the cooling effect of the downgoing plate on the Wadati–Benioff zone, as in NE Japan. However, there is a minor, localized heating effect caused by increased friction along the upper surface of the slab at higher subduction speeds. This effect is difficult to quantify, and indeed is disputed by some researchers.

Question 2.7 The arc–trench gap ranges from about 100 to 500 km, whereas the depth to the slab below the volcanic front varies from 80 to 200 km. In most cases, the arc–trench gap is between 100 and 300 km, and the slab is 80 to 150 km below the volcanic front.

Question 2.8 (a) Ordered back-arc spreading (Figure 2.9a) is the most akin to mid-ocean ridge spreading, being composed of linear ridge segments offset at transform faults, with new oceanic crust generated symmetrically on either side of the central rift. Figures 2.29a and 2.29b respectively.

(b) Disordered spreading (Figure 2.9b) lacks the symmetry of mid-ocean ridge spreading centres; segments of rift overlap and interfere in a more complex fashion. There is a wider area of spreading, and this area lacks clearly defined transform faults. In addition, there are places where lava is erupted at a single point rather than along a linear rift: these are shown as 'point sources' on Figure 2.29. Diffuse back-arc spreading (c) differs from mid-ocean ridges even more markedly than (b). In this case, there are no neat, linear ridges where new crust is produced. Instead, there are broad areas of magmatic activity, both intrusion and extrusion, which may correspond to clusters of 'point sources', or simply more diffuse magmatism.

(c) In terms of the characteristics outlined above, many back-arc spreading centres are difficult to define with certainty; the features associated with their slower spreading are more obscure than the striking linear mid-ocean ridge systems so prominent on the Dynamic Planet map. Their close association with adjacent arc systems, however, eases their identification.

Question 3.1 Substituting the given values, the Mg-number $= 100 \times (6.4/40)/((6.4/40) + (8.3/72)) = 100 \times 0.16/(0.16 + 0.115) = 58$, to two significant figures.

Question 3.2 (a) Water content decreases fairly steadily from about 6 to 2% between about 20 and 75 km. (b) The small amount of chlorite disappears, and the proportions of lawsonite and amphibole decrease; amphibole is no longer present beneath about 80 km.

Question 4.1 (a) Although the occasional point strays across the drawn boundaries, the Skaros rocks belong to the medium-K group. (b) Samples 181 and 180 are basalts, 182 and 178 are basaltic andesites, 171 is an andesite, and 153 is a dacite.

Question 4.2 The analysis of sample 178 has 7.84% FeO_t, 4.35% MgO, 3.03% Na_2O and 1.04% K_2O. The total alkali content is therefore $3.03\% + 1.04\% = 4.07\%$. The first step in plotting these data on Figure 4.3 is to normalize the data to a total of 100%, so

$$A = (4.07/(7.84 + 4.35 + 4.07)) \times 100\% = 25.0\%$$

$$F = (7.84/(7.84 + 4.35 + 4.07)) \times 100\% = 48.2\%$$

$$M = (4.35/(7.84 + 4.35 + 4.07)) \times 100\% = 26.8\%$$

The rock analysis therefore plots below the black boundary on Figure 4.3, confirming that this sample can be classified as calc-alkaline.

Question 4.3 (a) Using the definition Mg-number $= 100 \times En/(En + Fs)$, we have an Mg-number for this crystal of $100 \times 47.1/(47.1 + 12.4) = 79.2$. (b) The approximate composition is $En_{38}Fs_{22}Wo_{40}$, giving an Mg-number of 63.3. Note that the En, Fs and Wo contents should add up to 100.

Question 4.4 (a) As the Al_2O_3 content of the basalt and the andesite are about the same (c. 18.5%) the extract must also have c. 18.5% Al_2O_3. If this were not the case, the fractionated liquid would have a different Al_2O_3 content. For example, removal of only olivine, which contains no Al_2O_3, from the basalt would produce liquids with more than 18.5% Al_2O_3.

(b) Plagioclase has 29 to 35% Al_2O_3, while olivine and augite have hardly any (0 and 1 to 4%, respectively). A mineral assemblage with 18.5% Al_2O_3 must, therefore, contain a lot of plagioclase. To a rough approximation, 50 to 60% plagioclase and 50 to 40% olivine + augite would have the requisite amount of alumina.

(c) At c. 57% SiO_2, the Al_2O_3 content of the lavas start to decrease with increasing SiO_2 instead of staying constant, as was the case for the lavas with less than 57% SiO_2. This would be possible if the composition of the mineral extract changed significantly at 57% SiO_2. This is a likely possibility, as Figure 4.5 showed that orthopyroxene joins the crystallizing assemblage at around 57% SiO_2.

Question 4.5   (a) TiO_2 is abundant in titanomagnetite; FeO_t is high in titanomagnetite but also occurs in the ferromagnesian silicates (olivine, augite and orthopyroxene in this case); P_2O_5 is abundant only in apatite. So, fractional crystallization should cause TiO_2 to increase until titanomagnetite starts to crystallize, when TiO_2 will decrease due to the removal of titanomagnetite. Similarly, FeO_t should decrease strongly once titanomagnetite starts to crystallize. Apatite controls the behaviour of P_2O_5; fractional crystallization in the absence of apatite will lead to an increase in P_2O_5 but once apatite starts to be removed, P_2O_5 contents will drop.

(b) The trends in Figure 4.10 suggest that titanomagnetite fractionation starts at around 56% SiO_2 (TiO_2 and FeO_t decrease), and apatite fractionation starts at around 60% SiO_2 (P_2O_5 levels off). This is consistent with the observation that titanomagnetite and apatite are typically found as phenocrysts once SiO_2 has reached these values. Note that ilmenite also removes TiO_2 effectively, but this mineral is not found in Santorini's lavas until SiO_2 reaches about 66% (Figure 4.5).

Question 4.6   (a)   According to Equation 4.5:

$$D = 0.60 \times 0.01 + 0.10 \times 2.0 + 0.30 \times 6.2$$

$$D = 0.0060 + 0.20 + 1.86$$

$$D = 2.066$$

or $D = 2.1$, to two significant figures.

(b) According to the definition of the bulk partition coefficient (Equation 4.4) and the result $D = 2.1$, the concentration of Ni in the mineral assemblage will be 2.1 times that in the co-existing liquid.

Question 4.7 See completed Table below (Table A4.1).

Table A4.1 Normalized liquid composition C_l/C_0 as a function of the fraction of liquid remaining, F, during Rayleigh fractionation with bulk partition coefficient D.

F	$D = 3$	$D = 2$	$D = 1$	$D = 0.5$	$D = 0$
1.0	1.00	1.00	1.00	1.00	1.00
0.9	0.81	0.90	1.00	1.05	1.11
0.8	0.64	0.80	1.00	1.12	1.25
0.7	0.49	0.70	1.00	1.20	1.43
0.6	0.36	0.60	1.00	1.29	1.67
0.5	0.25	0.50	1.00	1.41	2.00
0.4	0.16	0.40	1.00	1.58	2.50
0.3	0.09	0.30	1.00	1.83	3.33
0.2	0.04	0.20	1.00	2.24	5.00
0.1	0.01	0.10	1.00	3.16	10.00

Question 4.8 See the completed Figure below (Figure A4.1).

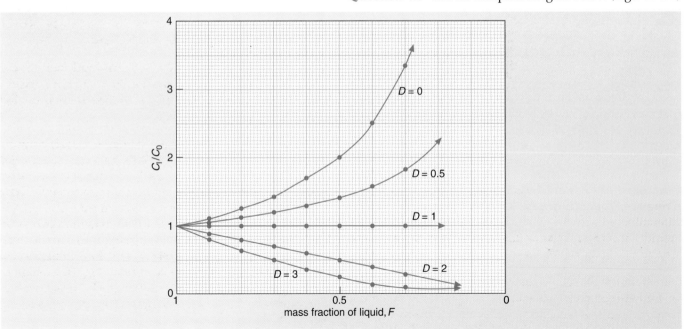

Figure A4.1 Answer to Question 4.8.

Question 4.9 (a) Here, $C_0 = 5$ ppm and $C_1 = 16$ ppm, so $16 = 5F^{(D_{Rb}-1)} = 5F^{-1} = 5/F$ hence $F = 5/16 = 0.3125$. That is,

> • Page 147, Question 4.9 (a), line 2: Part of the equation (the numerical phrase "-1" in the exponent "D_{Rb-1}") shown has been accidentally subscripted. The first part of the answer should read as follows:
>
> Here, $C_0 = 5$ppm and $C_1 = 16$ppm, so $16 = 5F^{(D_{Rb} - 1)} = 5F^{-1} = 5/F$ hence $F = 5/16 = 0.3125$.

(a) $F = 0.3125$ so $C_1 = 100\,(0.3125)^{(2-1)} = 100 \times 0.3125 = 31.25$ ppm. The andesite should contain 31.25 ppm Ni according to the Rayleigh fractionation equation. Again this result could also have been found from Figure A4.1, with $F = 0.31$ and $D = 2$ curve to give $C_1/C_0 = 0.31$, which, with $C_0 = 100$ ppm, gives $C_1 = 31$ ppm. This is in agreement with the calculation based on Rb in (a), so we can confirm that fractional crystallization is the process linking the basalt and andesite.

Question 4.10 The gradient of a straight line on a log-log plot is determined using a ruler to measure the 'rise' and 'run' of the line, not by reading off trace element concentrations from the axes of the graph as you would do on a linear plot. Thus, from Figure 4.13b, the gradient in this case is (see Figure A4.2) the measured vertical distance divided by the measured horizontal distance, i.e. −1.

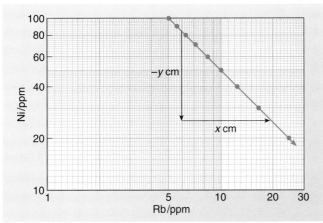

Figure A4.2 Diagram showing the measurements required to determine the slope of a line.

Question 4.11 Ni partitions most strongly into olivine and titanomagnetite and is also compatible in orthopyroxene and augite. Likewise, V (vanadium) and Sc (scandium) partition strongly into augite and titanomagnetite.

Question 4.12 For the basalt, $Ce_N = 17$ and $Yb_N = 8.5$, giving $(Ce/Yb)_N = 2$. (Do not worry if you read off slightly different values from Figure 4.16; your value of $(Ce/Yb)_N$ should have been close to 2.) Similarly for the andesite, $(Ce/Yb)_N = 65/20 = 3.25$.

Question 4.13 From Figure 4.17, the partition coefficient for Eu between plagioclase and liquid is about five times greater than the partition coefficients for Sm and Gd between plagioclase and liquid. When plagioclase is a fractionating mineral, Eu will be less incompatible than Sm and Gd, resulting in less enrichment of Eu in the differentiated magmas.

4 Careful measurements in reading off figure 4.16 should give results that are close to (a) Eu/Eu* = 10.5/11.2 = 0.94; (b) Eu/Eu* = ?6; (c) Eu/Eu* = 19.5/27 = 0.72.

Question 4.15 The greater the negative europium anomaly, i.e. the smaller Eu/Eu*, the greater the amount of plagioclase fractionation that has occurred. Thus the andesite is more fractionated than the basaltic andesite, and this accords with all your earlier work on fractional crystallization in the Santorini magmas.

Question 4.16 (a) The Mg-numbers are $100 \times 47/(47 + 9) = 84$ and $100 \times 43/(43 + 18) = 70$. Figure 4.8 implies that these crystals grew from magmas with about 6.5 to 7.5% MgO and 1 to 4% MgO. (b) The more calcic plagioclase most probably grew from basalt ($< 52\%$ SiO_2) or basaltic andesite (52 to 56% SiO_2). The sodic plagioclase most probably grew from andesite (56 to 63% SiO_2) or dacite ($> 63\%$ SiO_2).

Question 4.17 In the case of Ruapehu, Rb/Zr appeared to be an index of crustal contamination, so $^{87}Sr/^{86}Sr$ would be expected to increase at the same time as Rb/Zr. Figure 4.29 shows that this is the case: Rb/Zr correlates with $^{87}Sr/^{86}Sr$, and $^{87}Sr/^{86}Sr$ increases as SiO_2 increases.

Question 4.18 (a) (i) and (ii) Since silicic crust has higher $^{87}Sr/^{86}Sr$ and Rb/Sr ratios than basalt, crustal contamination will lead to an increase in both of these ratios within the magma. (b) (i) During fractional crystallization, isotope ratios do not change (Section 4.4.1) so $^{87}Sr/^{86}Sr$ remains constant. (ii) Rb is an incompatible trace element, while Sr is a compatible trace element (Section 4.2.4). Thus, Rb increases during fractional crystallization whereas Sr remains constant or decreases. Consequently, Rb/Sr increases during fractional crystallization.

Question 4.19 The data form a scattered but curved array that becomes flatter as Rb/Sr increases. This is consistent with AFC (cf. Figure 4.30). Basalt-crust mixing would give a straight-line trend.

Question 4.20 (a) Plagioclase contains a high alumina concentration, so plagioclase-absent fractional crystallization will cause Al_2O_3 to increase, whereas plagioclase-dominated fractional crystallization will cause Al_2O_3 to decrease (cf. Figure 4.9, Section 4.2.3). (b) FeO_t is present in the ferromagnesian silicates olivine and pyroxene, as well as the spinel mineral found in hydrous experiments. Fractional crystallization dominated by these minerals will lead to FeO_t decreasing with decreasing MgO (also high in ferromagnesian silicates), whereas plagioclase fractionation will counteract this effect, with the possibility of increasing FeO_t.

Question 5.1 Two of the listed pieces of geological evidence do *not* corroborate specific predictions of the dynamic wedge model. They are (iii) and (vii).

(i) Compression in the toe region is one of the responses to a low taper, and will form imbricate stacks and folds.

(ii) Extensional faults occur when a prism is trying to reduce its angle of taper by extending and thinning.

(iii) High-pressure metamorphic rocks exposed in the toe region of the prism are not predicted by the dynamic wedge model. Their occurrence in the toe region is unusual and would most likely reflect some kind of channel flow in a mélange.

(iv) The surface slopes and general form of accretionary prisms conform quite closely to the predictions of the dynamic wedge model.

(v) Figure 5.8 shows that exhumation would occur during continued subduction according to the dynamic wedge model.

(vi) High-pressure metamorphic rocks are commonly observed exposed at the rear of accretionary prisms by exhumation from depth, as predicted by the model.

(vii) Mud volcanoes are not a specific prediction of the dynamic wedge model; in fact, they can be associated with any thick pile of unconsolidated, fluid-rich sediments.

(viii) Both stratigraphic ages and depth of metamorphism are predicted to increase from the toe to the rear of the prism in the model.

Question 5.2 It will take $150\,\text{km} / (10^{-5}\,\text{km cm}^{-1} \times 5\,\text{cm yr}^{-1})$ $= 3 \times 10^6$ years $= 3$ million years.

Question 6.1 (a) To the east of the Romeral Fault Zone, the basement comprises Precambrian to Mesozoic igneous and metamorphic rocks, while west of the fault zone the basement is typical of oceanic crust (basalts, gabbros). (b) Mesozoic plutons in the Central Cordillera generally give way to Tertiary plutons in the Western Cordillera, i.e. the plutons become younger towards the west.

Question 6.2 (a) Extrusive (eruption of basaltic lavas at the surface) and intrusive (addition of plutonic rocks at depth). [Note that intrusion occurs on a range of scales, from kilometre-scale gabbro bodies to mafic dykes less than a metre wide.]

(b) *Extrusive:* Pillow basalts (basaltic lava erupted underwater) form the top of the pile; some of the ultramafic rocks directly underlying these basalts may also have erupted at the surface, though it is common for magmas not quite reaching the surface to form horizontal sills at shallow levels. On Figure 6.4 their tabular forms are very similar to lava flows.

Intrusive: Intrusions occur at all levels, including the shallow mafic and ultramafic sills mentioned above. Minor mafic intrusions at high levels may also take the form of small lensoid bodies. Lower down, larger mafic magma chambers form gabbroic plutons when they crystallize. As shown in the Figure, these commonly contain a mixture of massive, granular gabbro, and layered gabbro on the walls and base of the chamber. This layering results from the accumulation of crystals settling out of the magma. Similar layering, known as 'cumulate layering', occurs in some ultramafic rocks (dunites and pyroxenites) underlying the gabbros.

Question 6.3 Because the plateau was obducted very soon after its formation (< 25 million years), the whole edifice was still relatively warm and therefore buoyant compared to other oceanic plateaux. This is the most likely reason for the preservation of deeper levels than usual onland; in a sense, the whole plateau was 'riding higher' when it collided with the margin of western Colombia, so it wasn't only the highest levels that were scraped off and exposed.

Question 6.4 (a) Chert and basalt. (The peridotite/serpentinite are also of Jurassic age, and could potentially be just as old.)

(b) Chert is generally characteristic of deep-water deposition with little or no input of terrigenous (continental) detritus. [Commonly thinly bedded, it is mainly composed of the microscopic skeletons of radiolaria, siliceous planktonic organisms.] Pillow basalt is indicative of submarine volcanism.

(c) Proximal (near-shelf) turbidites in the late Jurassic, and limestone in the Cretaceous, attest to episodes of shallower-water sedimentation. Clastic sediments from the late Jurassic onwards imply a landmass nearby as a source for the detritus, which could have been either an oceanic arc, or the North American continent. Turbidites imply sedimentation into relatively deep water on steep slopes — perhaps the edge of a continental shelf.

Question 6.5 (a) It would take only 2.1 Ma: $(7\,\text{km}/100\,\text{km Ma}^{-1}) \times 30\,\text{km} = 2.1$ Ma. (b) The blueschist facies rock was buried from the time of peak metamorphism to exposure and erosion $(118 - 60 = 58\,\text{Ma})$. An additional 2 Ma must be added to this total for its initial burial (from part (a) above); i.e. 60 Ma in total.

Question 7.1 (a) (i) Granite has a higher proportion of quartz than does quartz monzonite. (ii) Tonalite has a higher proportion of plagioclase than does granodiorite. (iii) Tonalite has a much higher proportion of quartz than does gabbro. (iv) Quartz diorite has a lower proportion of quartz and a higher proportion of plagioclase than does granodiorite. (b) Granite, quartz monzodiorite, gabbro.

Question 7.2 (a) All but one of the rocks from Finger Bay have less than 60% SiO_2; the opposite is true for those from Senal Blanca. The island arc example is therefore less silicic than the continental margin pluton.

(b) The island arc pluton is tholeiitic, whereas the continental margin complex is calc-alkaline.

(c) Quartz is more abundant in the rocks of Senal Blanca than in those of Finger Bay — as you might predict from the SiO_2 contents. Granites, granodiorites and tonalites are found at Senal Blanca, while Finger Bay contains gabbros, diorites, quartz diorites, quartz monzodiorites and quartz monzonites.

Question 7.3 (a) Active volcanism occurs in four distinct regions: between latitudes 5° N and 2° S (in Colombia and Ecuador), 16° and 28° S (mainly southern Peru and northern Chile), 31° and 46° S (central Chile), and 49° and 54° S (southern Chile). These are referred to as the Northern Volcanic Zone (NVZ), Central Volcanic Zone (CVZ), Southern Volcanic Zone (SVZ) and Austral Volcanic Zone (AVZ) respectively and you should label Figure 7.6a accordingly.

(b) The spacing of contours on the Wadati–Benioff zone (Figure 7.6a) shows that the downgoing slab appears segmented, with steep dips (about 30°) coinciding with the volcanic zones, and gentler dips (about 10°) in so-called 'flat-slab' zones. These slab segments are contrasted in the cross-sections of Figure 7.6b. Note that the flat-slab zones correlate with sections of the Andes lacking recent volcanism.

(c) The oldest oceanic lithosphere entering the Peru–Chile trench is Eocene in age (Figure 7.6c), subducting beneath southern Peru and northern Chile. Subducting lithosphere becomes younger both to the north and south, towards the Galápagos and Chile Rise spreading ridges respectively. These ridges are characterized by recently formed, buoyant oceanic lithosphere. Two other prominent ridges, the Nazca and Juan Fernandez Ridges, are also made of relatively buoyant oceanic material.

(d) Most of the Andean crust is at least 30 km thick — typical for continental crust. Thicker crust (up to 70 km) underlies the central Andes (parts of Peru, Bolivia, NW Argentina and northern Chile).

(e) The Andean range broadens from a narrow band of mountains in Chile and Argentina to the central Andes in the southern part of Bolivia, before narrowing again to the north-west. The western boundary is sharp, with a narrow coastal plain. Two distinct types of topography can be seen on the eastern edge of the mountain belt: first, a series of fine parallel ridges curving round the broadest part of the range — the sub-Andean fold and thrust belt; and secondly, a series of isolated ridges splaying off the foothills in Argentina — the Sierras Pampeanas, which are uplifted basement blocks. Finally, there is the striking high plateau in the core of the central Andes, the Altiplano.

Question 7.4 (a) The Coastal Batholith has an estimated volume of 10^6 km^3 and was emplaced over a period of 70 Ma, giving an average rate of intrusion into the crust of about 10^6 km^3/70 Ma = 1.43×10^4 km^3 Ma^{-1} (or 1.43×10^{-2} km^3 yr^{-1}). [As the information given is accurate only to 1 significant figure, the answer should also be reported to that accuracy: 1×10^4 km^3 Ma^{-1}]. (b) The intrusion rate was 1.43×10^4 km^3 Ma^{-1} (from part (a)), and the batholith is 1600 km long. This gives an intrusion rate of 1.43×10^4 km^3 Ma^{-1}/1600 km = 9 km^3 Ma^{-1} km^{-1}.

Question 7.5 The total global crustal growth rates at subduction zones are: (a) 30 km^3 Ma^{-1} km^{-1} × 37 000 km = 1.1×10^6 km^3 Ma^{-1}; (b) 60 km^3 Ma^{-1} km^{-1} × 37 000 km = 2.2×10^6 km^3 Ma^{-1}.

Question 7.6 The volume of the continental crust is 7.8×10^9 km^3, and the age of the Earth is 4.55×10^9 years. The long-term growth rate of continental crust is 7.8×10^9 km^3/4.55×10^9 yr = 1.7 km^3 yr^{-1} = 1.7×10^6 km^3 Ma^{-1}.

Acknowledgements

Every effort has been made to trace all copyright owners, but if any has been inadvertently overlooked, we will be pleased to make the necessary arrangements at the earliest opportunity. Grateful acknowledgement is made to the following sources for permission to reproduce material within this Block:

Figures 2.2, 2.28 D. E. Karig (1971) 'Origin and development of marginal basins in the Western Pacific', *Journal of Geophysical Research*, **76**, American Geophysical Union; *Figures 2.3–2.5, 2.8, 2.10, 2.14, 2.15a,b, 2.16b, 2.18a, 2.29, 2.32, 5.3c, 5.4, 5.5b–d, 5.8* E. M. Moores and R. J. Twiss, *Tectonics*, © 1995 W. H. Freeman and Co.; *Figure 2.6* © R. D. Van der Hilst, Department of Earth, Atmospheric and Planetary Sciences, MIT; *Figure 2.7* P. Kearey and F. J. Vine *Global Tectonics*, © 1990 Blackwell; *Figure 2.9* J. B. Gill, *Orogenic Andesites and Plate Tectonics*, © 1981 Springer-Verlag; *Figure 2.12* S. M. Peacock (2000) 'Thermal structure and metamorphic evolution …', American Geophysical Union; *Figures 2.17, 2.18b, 2.19b, 5.3a,b, 6.6b–d* John Platt, University College London; *Figure 2.18c* Steve Ellen, USGS (retired); *Figure 2.19a* © Wushangting Mud Volcano Nature Reserve, Kaosiung County, Taiwan, ROC; *Figure 2.19c,d* A. Milne, Anatomy of a mud volcano, Monday 3 March 1997, Internet Express, Trinidad; *Figure 2.20a* Trinidad Lake Asphalt, Lake Asphalt of Trinidad and Tobago (1978) Ltd; *Figure 2.20b,c* Tar Formations on Pitch Lake, Trinidad, © Jim Steinhart; *Figure 2.20d* H. H. Suter (1951) *Colonial Geology and Mineral Resources*, **2**; *Figure 2.23a* M. Barton and J. P. P. Huijsmans (1986) 'Post caldera dacites from Santorini volcanic complex, Aegean Sea, Greece', *Contributions to Mineralogy and Petrology*, **94**, No. 4, Springer-Verlag; *Figures 2.24, 2.26, 4.4, 4.20, 4.21, 4.25, 7.2* Stephen Blake, Open University; *Figure 2.25* M. J. Le Bas *et al.* (1986) 'A chemical classification of volcanic rocks …', *Journal of Petrology*, **27**, No. 3, Oxford University Press; *Figure 2.30* SOEST, University of Hawaii; *Figure 3.1* J. Nakajima *et al.* (2001) 'Three dimensional structure of V_p, V_s and V_p/V_s …', *Journal of Geophysical Research*, **106**, No. B10, American Geophysical Union; *Figure 3.5* S. Poli and M. W. Schmidt (1995) 'H_2O transport and release in subduction zones …', *Journal of Geophysical Research*, **100**, No. B11, American Geophysical Union; *Figures 3.7, 3.8* D. W. Peate *et al.* (2001) 'U series isotope data on Lau Basin …' *Journal of Petrology*, **42**, No. 8, Oxford University Press; *Figure 4.5* T. H. Druitt *et al.* (1999/2000) 'Santorini Volcano', *Geological Society Memoirs*, No. 19, Geological Society Publishing House; *Figure 4.33* R. J. Kinzler, J. M. Donnelly-Nolan and T. L. Grove (2000) 'Late Holocene hydrous mafic magmatism …', *Contributions to Mineralogy and Petrology*, **138**, Springer-Verlag; *Figure 4.35* J. P. P. Huijsmans and M. Barton (1989) 'Polybaric geochemical evolution of two shield volcanoes from Santorini …', *Journal of Petrology*, **30**, No. 3, Oxford University Press; *Figure 5.2* © Professor Martin Meschede, Institute of Geology, University of Tuebingen; *Figures 5.5a, 6.9* J. P. Platt (1993) 'Exhumation of high-pressure rocks …', *Terra Nova*, **5**, Blackwell; *Figure 5.6* USGS and NASA Landsat data: images provided by John Platt, University College London; *Figures 6.1a, 7.6d, 7.7* US National Intelligence Mapping Agency, GTOP030 digital elevation data; map designed by Steve Drury for the Course Team; *Figure 6.1b* G. F. Marriner and D. Millward (1984) 'The petrology and geochemistry of Cretaceous to Recent volcanism …', *Journal of the Geological Society*, **141**, The Geological Society, London; *Figure 6.2* J. A. Aspden *et al.* (1987) 'Geometrical control of subduction-related magmatism …', *Journal of the Geological Society*, **144**, The Geological Society, London; *Figure 6.4* A. C. Kerr *et al.* (1998) 'The international structure of oceanic plateaus …', *Tectonophysics*, **292**, Elsevier Science; *Figure 6.5* U. Ring *et al.* (1998) 'Franciscan complex deformation', in U. Ring and M. T. Brandon (eds), *Exhumation Processes: Normal Faulting, Ductile Flow and Erosion*, Geological Society Special Publication No. 154, Geological Society Publishing House; *Figure 6.6a* D. Alt and D. W. Hyndman (2000) 'The magnificent coast', *Roadside Geology of Northern and Central California*, Mountain Press Publishing, © 2000 David Alt and Donal W. Hyndman; *Figure 6.8a* Tom Argles, Open University; *Figure 6.10d* A. Miyashiro (1973) 'Paired and unpaired metamorphic belts', *Tectonophysics*, **17**, Elsevier Science; *Figure 7.1a* I. S. E. Carmichael *et al.* (1974) *Igneous Petrology*, McGraw-Hill; *Figure 7.1b* G. C. Brown *et al.* (1984) 'The geochemical characteristics of granitoids in contrasting areas', *Journal of the Geological Society*, **141**, The Geological Society, London; *Figure 7.4a* S. Mahlburg Kay *et al.* (1983) 'Tholeiitic Aleutian arc plutonism …', *Contributions to Mineralogy and Petrology*, **82**, Springer-Verlag; *Figure 7.6a* A. M. Ziegler *et al.* (1981) 'Palaeoclimate, sedimentation and continental accretion', *Philosophical Transactions of the Royal Society*, **A301**, The Royal Society; *Figure 7.6b* M. Barazangi and B. L. Isacks (1976) 'Spatial distribution of earthquakes and subduction …', *Geology*, **4**, No. 11, The Geological Society of America; *Figure 7.9* A. Reymer and G. Schubert (1984) 'Phanerozoic addition rates to the continental crust and crustal growth', *Tectonics*, **3** (joint publication of American Geophysical Union and European Geophysical Society).

Index